REMBRANDT: *Experimental Etcher*

REMBRANDT:

Experimental Etcher

MUSEUM OF FINE ARTS, BOSTON

PIERPONT MORGAN LIBRARY, NEW YORK

Copyright © 1969 by the Museum of Fine Arts, Boston, Mass.
Library of Congress Catalogue Card No. 77-93138
Type set by Typographic House, Inc., Boston, Massachusetts
Printed by The Meriden Gravure Company, Meriden, Connecticut
Designed by Carl F. Zahn

Dates of the Exhibition:

Museum of Fine Arts, Boston   Oct. 1, 1969 – Nov. 9, 1969
Pierpont Morgan Library, New York   Nov. 26, 1969 – Jan. 10, 1970

Lenders

Allen Memorial Art Museum, Oberlin College, Oberlin, Ohio

The Art Institute of Chicago, Chicago, Illinois

The Boston Public Library, Boston, Massachusetts

Fogg Art Museum, Harvard University, Cambridge, Massachusetts

The Library of Congress, Washington, D.C.

The Metropolitan Museum of Art, New York, New York

Museum of Fine Arts, Boston, Massachusetts

National Gallery of Art, Washington, D.C.

North Carolina Museum of Art, Raleigh, North Carolina

Pierpont Morgan Library, New York, New York

Private Collection

Lessing J. Rosenwald, Jenkintown, Pennsylvania

Yale University Art Gallery, New Haven, Connecticut

Acknowledgements

It is not possible to prepare a major exhibition without the help and cooperation of many institutions and individuals. Before the selection of prints for the exhibition was made, we asked the public institutions and various private collectors to help us compile a census of Rembrandt etchings in American collections. We are extremely grateful to the curatorial staffs and to the individual collectors throughout the United States for the warmth and helpfulness of their response.

We wish above all to thank the lenders to the exhibition who with unstinting generosity acceded to our every request for loans of the utmost importance. Their genuine interest in the exhibition has been most gratifying; their support, invaluable. We are grateful for the time and detailed information given by various persons, in particular the following: Miss Janet Byrne, The Metropolitan Museum of Art; Fred Cain, Alverthorpe Gallery; Alan Fern, Library of Congress; Egbert Haverkamp-Begemann, Yale University Art Gallery and the National Gallery of Art; Sinclair H. Hitchings, Boston Public Library; Harold Joachim, The Art Institute of Chicago; Miss Ruth S. Magurn, Fogg Art Museum; John J. McKendry, The Metropolitan Museum of Art; Lessing J. Rosenwald, Alverthorpe Gallery; Miss Katharine Shepard, National Gallery of Art; Alan Shestack, Yale University Art Gallery.

Special thanks are due Christopher White of P.&D. Colnaghi & Company, Ltd., London, who though working on the similar exhibition held at the British Museum, nevertheless gave freely of his time and knowledge in our behalf. With signal generosity, he and K.T. Boon also made available to us the proofs of their forthcoming *catalogue raisonné* of Rembrandt's etchings. We are much indebted to both of them.

We also wish to thank various helpful persons within the collaborating institutions themselves. The Pierpont Morgan Library: Frederick B. Adams, Jr., Director; Mrs. Ruth S. Kraemer and A.J. Yow. The Museum of Fine Arts: Perry T. Rathbone, Director; Miss Patricia Alward; Francis W. Dolloff; Miss Stephanie Loeb; Miss Susan Okie; Roy Perkinson; Mrs. John Shlien; Mrs. Anne B. Smith; Mrs. Elliott S. Topkins; Miss Barbara Valentine and Carl Zahn.

The catalogue was prepared jointly by Felice Stampfle, Pierpont Morgan Library; Eleanor A. Sayre, Sue W. Reed and Clifford S. Ackley, Museum of Fine Arts. The essay on papers used by Rembrandt was written by Mrs. Reed.

Eleanor A. Sayre, *Curator of Prints and Drawings, Museum of Fine Arts, Boston*
Felice Stampfle, *Curator of Drawings and Prints, Pierpont Morgan Library, New York*

Introduction

No prints are more widely known and valued than those by Rembrandt. They have been copied and imitated for generations. The copper plates which survived his death were posthumously reprinted until the most popular ones, painfully worn, could produce no more than a distorted version of the original image. Even then, the plates were not allowed to die but were reworked into some semblance of what they once had been and continued to be printed and sold. But possibly the best witness to the esteem in which Rembrandt's work has been held is the number of fine early impressions which have been treasured and carefully preserved, passing from hand to hand down through the three centuries which have elapsed since Rembrandt's death.

One cannot be wholly aware of the beauty of a Rembrandt etching until one sees an impression taken when the work on the copper plate was fresh. Then all the printed lines register with the clarity which they were intended to have and are in an exact tonal balance in relation to the paper. Many of the prints, particularly the later ones, cannot be understood by knowing them in a single fine impression. For it is only by examining side by side impressions taken at various stages in the development of the plate that one becomes keenly aware of the extent to which a great artist's conception of his subject can alter as he works on the plate. And it is only by seeing various impressions of the same state, printed on different kinds of paper, or specially inked to bring out alternative aspects of the subject, that one perceives how creative a role the very act of printing assumed for Rembrandt. The manner in which he worked his plates, the way they were inked and wiped, and the paper he selected were each important.

One can understand a Rembrandt etching better by seeing a number of impressions of it than by viewing merely one. But, insofar as we are aware, no exhibition has attempted to demonstrate this until 1969, the three hundredth anniversary of his death. In many ways this exhibition is a transatlantic version of the memorable show held at the British Museum in London earlier this year under the auspices of the Arts Council. Organized by Christopher White, that exhibition drew primarily upon the collections of the great European print rooms. The idea of assembling such an exhibition in the United States, however, had for some time been independently entertained by the Pierpont Morgan Library, New York, and the Museum of Fine Arts, Boston; and in 1967 when it was learned that both institutions were pursuing a similar idea, it was agreed to join forces.

Relying solely upon the resources of American collections, this exhibition, like its London counterpart, focuses on the period from about 1647 until the end of Rembrandt's etching activity in the early 1660's. For it is in these later years that Rembrandt, in full command of his medium, produced his most experimental prints. Twenty-eight subjects have been selected from the more than three hundred which Rembrandt etched. They are exhibited in one hundred and eighteen impressions which display these subjects in as full a progression of states as could be mustered from American collections. In many instances, a number of impressions of the same state are shown.

The greatness of these works scarcely needs to be mentioned, far less elaborated upon. What has received much less attention than it deserves is the painter's restless probing for the most expressive graphic means that would depict his changing concept of a subject.

When the successive states of an etching are looked at carefully, they record very clearly the ways in which Rembrandt changed his mind about his composition or about the meaning of his print. In a print like *Clement de Jonghe* (Cat. No. VIII) it is possible to follow the subtle though important changes Rembrandt made in his composition through successive states, as well as the marked psychological alterations which occur in the characterization of the sitter. The first state is for the most part lightly etched, so that the lines print on white paper as almost translucent grays. The expression of the printseller, with his unevenly set eyes, seems reserved, indeed withdrawn. Rembrandt appears to have been satisfied with the print in this stage, at least initially; it is the state most commonly found in American collections, some thirteen impressions being recorded in museums here.

The second state preserves much of the earlier luminosity, but Rembrandt changed the character of the print. Firmer outlining of de Jonghe's cloak and chair, the darkening of his hat and the shadowing of his face all give the composition a strength it had lacked. In addition, there is now a powerful sense of the individuality of the sitter, concentrated in rigid hands and shoulders and intense burning face.

In the third state Rembrandt added an arch, which increases the stability of his composition. He further shaded the right side of de Jonghe's face, which softens the crooked effect of his right eye, but also diminishes the great individuality of the portrait so evident in the preceding state.

In the fourth state Rembrandt strengthened and darkened the arch and gave the print a new, quite different compositional balance by adding dark shadows to de Jonghe's clothes and deepening the shadow cast on the wall to the left of his chair.

Both of the great drypoints *Christ Presented to the People* and *Christ Crucified between the Two Thieves* were radically altered in the fifth and fourth states, respectively. It has been suggested that Rembrandt made these changes because the fugitive drypoint lines had weakened. It is quite true that in some impressions the loss is appreciable, but to attribute such a major reworking of the two plates to this single cause is to be unaware of the directions in which Rembrandt had been altering these masterpieces in their earlier states.

In the first state of *Christ Presented to the People* (Cat. No. XIV), it is the response of individuals to an event in the Bible which seems to have interested Rembrandt. Men, women and even children stare at Jesus with curiosity, hatred or mockery. They stand beside Him on the tribunal, peer down at Him from the windows of the monumental hall, crowd the stairway, and spread out across the courtyard.

In the following state Rembrandt made changes to the right side of the building, turning it into a complex barrier of light and shadow which directs one's attention back to the figure of Jesus.

It is in the fifth and sixth states (neither of them available in the United States) that Rembrandt made his major alterations to the plate. He strengthened the pattern of sunlight and shadow throughout the great building. He increased the size of the group at the left and eliminated all the figures standing in front of the tribunal, letting its blank front wall act as a great pedestal for Christ. Finally, in the seventh state, he achieved what he seems to have been looking for earlier – a just and very complex balance of importance between the Christ whom Pilate has placed on trial and the ordinary individuals who at the moment are deciding to condemn Him to death.

In *Christ Crucified between the Two Thieves* (Cat. No. XIII), Rembrandt seems to have had to resolve the same dichotomy: his perceptive interest in how the Crucifixion would affect diverse human beings and his realization that this concern must not be allowed to diffuse the majesty of the event. In the first state, as Jesus surrenders His spirit and the three-hour darkness begins to be lifted from the earth, a part of the mocking crowd turns to flee; mounted soldiers watch stolidly; the centurion, suddenly believing, kneels; the Marys and the apostles grieve, each in his own fashion. In the first and second states, Rembrandt tried diminishing the force of the crowd – not by adding further work to the plate – but by darkening these half-formed groups of people in various ways, and to varying degrees, with tones of ink printed from the surface of the plate. In some impressions in order to emphasize the figure of Christ, he carefully wiped

clean the strong verticals of the wooden cross and the body of Jesus.

In the third state, Rembrandt modified the print, unifying the composition and changing its balance by adding considerable shading to the foreground and to figures throughout the crowd. The volume of light falling on the scene was reduced, and the group at the left now moves in a flickering light. It is in this state that Rembrandt signed and dated his plate.

In the radically altered fourth state (which may have been executed after an interval of several years), Rembrandt moved the event back in time so that Jesus is still alive and the profound darkness over the world, shot with light from heaven, falls principally on Christ. The attendant persons are now only half seen. What they feel must be grasped in part by an act of imagination.

In the history of printmaking, it has generally been professional printmakers who have perfected the technical aspects of etching, while it is primarily great painters who have expanded its limits. The latter, intent on what they had to say, worked the plate by whatever means were needed, however unorthodox, to give form to the images they had conceived.

In his later prints Rembrandt rarely employed etching by itself but usually in new and unexpected combinations with other techniques, especially drypoint. In the second state of the etching *Christ at Emmaus* (Cat. No. XIX), rather than rebiting the plate, Rembrandt made additions with a drypoint needle scratching directly into the copper. In the print, the pungent lines of drypoint overlie the airier etched lines of the basic design; they complete Jesus' face, increase the light emanating from Him and add substance to the huge canopy which Rembrandt had placed over the supper table to emphasize the importance of the event.

Rembrandt was the first printmaker to understand fully the potentialities of drypoint. On occasion he used its fleeting but powerful burr to give velvety shadows to an etching. In early impressions of the *Agony in the Garden* (Cat. No. XXIV), these strong black accents intimate the cloudy darkness which surrounds the moonlit confrontation of Christ and the compassionate angel.

Rembrandt would also combine drypoint with the incisive lines of engraving. In *Christ Crucified between the Two Thieves* (Cat. No. XIII), he used these techniques together to suggest the stark immediacy of the event and the terrible darkness.

In many prints, all three media – etching, engraving and drypoint – are used in combination. In the *Woman with the "Arrow"* (Cat. No. XXVIII), for example, Rembrandt blended them with an extraordinary painterly intelligence so that one is not aware of the diversity of means he used to suggest the soft roundness of the woman's flesh, the heavy material of the curtain behind her, or the fine quality of the bed linen and clothing.

The accidents occurring in the process of etching a copper plate, customarily corrected by meticulous craftsmen, were often brilliantly utilized by Rembrandt. In both *Clement de Jonghe* (Cat. No. VIII) and *Saint Jerome Reading in an Italian Landscape* (Cat. No. XII), the abraded surface left by the polishing of the plate was preserved by Rembrandt and prints as translucent tone. Random lines caused by defects in the etching ground laid on the plate, which are visible through the open window in the second and third states of *Rembrandt Drawing at a Window* (Cat. No. III), were incorporated into a landscape in the fourth state.

Rembrandt was able to burnish or scrape out rejected areas in a copper plate and hammer it back to its original level, removing all traces of former lines. But he did not always choose to do so. In the drastically reworked state of *Christ Crucified between the Two Thieves* (Cat. No. XIII), partly obliterated figures from the earlier states are retained, increasing the feeling of frightened confusion among the spectators. In the fifth state of *Christ Presented to the People* (Cat. No. XIV), when the crowd standing in front of the tribunal was scraped from the copper plate, a roughened area was left. This prints as an uneven tone by which Rembrandt suggests the mysterious character of the tribunal wall.

Much of Rembrandt's technique is not susceptible to analysis by either printmaker or connoisseur. His effects are too personal, too inventive, too closely blended.

The fourth state of *Christ Crucified between the Two Thieves* (Cat. No. XIII) is a profound and powerful work. But Rembrandt, still bent on exploring the possibilities of the plate, made even more beautiful and impressive prints by leaving carefully wiped surface tone on the plate. In a number of impressions this produces a dramatic darkness which intensifies the harshness of the tragedy. It is this masterly and imaginative use of tone which makes many of the impressions printed by Rembrandt himself unique and precious.

In impressions of the *"Negress" Lying Down* (Cat. No. XXVI), for example, one finds that additional surface ink had been applied with great care to the plate so that the subtleties of the contours of her body are delicately marked, and even the quality of her flesh suggested.

The portrait of *Jan Asselyn* was inked in various ways by Rembrandt to lend grace to an ungainly body. In an impression of the second state (Cat. No. 2), surface tone has been left in the background and the painter's clothing darkened so that his stocky body acquires an unexpected monumentality and his spirit, dignity.

Probably no two early impressions of *Christ with the Sick around Him* (Cat. No. IV) were printed alike. In this ambitious plate, on which Rembrandt seems to have worked for several years, tone gives the rocky background different painterly aspects; it also is used to vary the relationship of Jesus to the crowd or to single out one or another of the groups who importune Him.

In an impression of the *Presentation in the Temple* with little or no tone (Cat. No. 76), Joseph and his young wife are seen kneeling in the temple at Jerusalem, where in compliance with the law, they have come to present their firstborn son to the Lord. The aged Simeon has taken the baby in his arms and offers Him to the High Priest. Whereas in an impression with considerable tone (Cat. No. 77), Rembrandt obscures the two parents almost entirely and concentrates instead on Simeon, the infant Jesus and the two priests, so that the underlying theological import of the episode becomes plain. It had been decreed that Simeon, the holy and orthodox Jew, would not die until he had beheld the Christ with his own eyes. In the person of the infant whom he lifts with such tenderness towards the High Priest, he recognizes the "Glory of Israel" and the imminence of his own death.

Rembrandt was open to experiment not only in his working of copper plates and his manner of inking them, but also in his choice of papers. He was acutely sensitive to the inherent possibilities of various kinds of paper. He could, for example, let handmade European paper, with its slight irregularities and faint hue, suggest the breadth of sky in the *Landscape with Three Gabled Cottages beside a Road* (Cat. No. VI), or the quality of sunlight on stone in *Christ Preaching* (Cat. No. 43).

He printed some of the most beautiful impressions of *Saint Jerome Reading in an Italian Landscape* (Cat. No. 52) on common, unbleached "oatmeal" paper, whose sober color, so appropriate to the character of Saint Jerome, serves to bind together the light and dark components of the composition, including the lion with its rough, black mane and the Saint reading in the sun.

Occasionally Rembrandt used vellum, a material rarely used by other Dutch printmakers of his day. Its virtues for printing are sometimes difficult to judge in our own time since the years have wrinkled, yellowed or badly cockled many of the impressions he printed on this substance. Either the quality of the skins or the manner in which they were prepared seems to have made the vellum more absorbent to ink than, for example, the vellum sometimes used for printing books in Paris at the end of the fifteenth century. Rembrandt's printed lines take on something of the breadth and strength of those he drew on paper with a reed pen. The drypoint first state of *Saint Francis beneath a Tree, Praying* (Cat. No. 101) must have seemed to Rembrandt to require this extra forcefulness. Two of the five known impressions are printed on vellum and two more are on especially absorbent papers which likewise broaden the effect of the drypoint; one of these is possibly Indian in origin and the other undoubtedly Japanese.

The so-called Indian paper, which appears infrequently in Rembrandt's work, is to be seen in only one print in this exhibition, a first state of *Jan Asselyn* (Cat. No. 1). This is not the case, however, with imported Japanese paper. Rembrandt may have been attracted to it initially because of its exotic aspects: its Eastern origin, its preciousness and its silken quality. By 1647 Rembrandt was using Japanese paper for prints. It is true that he was not the only Dutch artist to use it: drawings on this kind of paper by artists in Rembrandt's circle such as Jan Lievens or Philips Koninck are relatively common. One other printmaker, Simon de Vlieger, tried it occasionally, for there are fine impressions on Japanese paper of his ten animal etchings in the British Museum and of a landscape in The Metropolitan Museum of Art.

But it was Rembrandt alone who fully sensed, as a great creative artist does, the stimulation of the new material; and he alone instinctively understood how to exploit it. Japanese paper was available to him in a variety of weights and textures, and in colors which could be very nearly white, golden or almost tan.

In the full length portrait, *Jan Six*, Rembrandt's friend leans against an open casement window to catch the light as he reads. An impression of the second state of this etching (Cat. No. 4) is printed on Japanese paper, whose warm color gives the illusion that the world outside is sunlit. This light enters his room illuminating the young merchant's face and hands, and touching the rich furnishings with glinting highlights. To cite another print, the almost white, translucent Japanese paper on which a first state of *Christ at Emmaus* (Cat. No. 87) is printed suggests of itself the quietness of that

mystical moment when two of His apostles first recognized the risen Christ.

Rembrandt sometimes used Japanese paper, as he did "oatmeal" paper, to provide an intermediate tonality in a composition. In a very early impression of *The Gold-weigher's Field* printed on white European paper (Cat. No. 28), the black touches of drypoint burr on the etched grove of trees are too pronounced, so that the recession of the grove into the middle distance is not convincing. In an equally early impression printed on Japanese paper (Cat. No. 27), the light golden hue modifies the overly sharp contrasts. These are further diminished by two other characteristics of Japanese paper which Rembrandt understood and exploited. This type of paper catches and prints any residual tone of ink left on the plate, so that the color of the paper appears darker than it is. Furthermore, because of its absorbency, Japanese paper broadens and softens both etched and drypoint lines, bringing them into greater harmony with each other and with the paper.

When one comes to know a Rembrandt etching in a range of impressions one sees how the print grew like a living entity under Rembrandt's hand, and how he conquered the problems it presented by experimenting with many possible solutions. Then one understands as never before the process of creating a great work of art.

Catalogue

The following abbreviations are used throughout the catalogue. The catalogue follows Hind in the definition of states. The measurements given are those of Biörklund and Barnard. All impressions exhibited are reproduced and are illustrated in the same size as the original prints, unless otherwise noted in the captions; the numbers correspond to those of the catalogue entries.

H.	Arthur M. Hind, *A Catalogue of Rembrandt's Etchings*. London, second edition, 1923, 2 vols.
B.	Adam Bartsch, *Catalogue raisonné de toutes les estampes qui forment l'oeuvre de Rembrandt* . . ., Vienna, 1797.
Mz.	Ludwig Münz, *Rembrandt's Etchings*, London, 1952, 2 vols.
BB.	George Biörklund and Osbert H. Barnard, *Rembrandt's Etchings: True and False*, Stockholm, second edition, 1968.
White	Christopher White, *Rembrandt as an Etcher*, London, revised edition, 1969, 2 vols.
L.	Frits Lugt, *Les Marques de Collections de dessins & d'estampes*, Amsterdam, 1921; Supplement, The Hague, 1956.
Heawood	Edward Heawood, *Watermarks*, Hilversum, 1950.
Churchill	W.A. Churchill, *Watermarks in the XVII and XVIII Centuries*, Amsterdam, 1935.

I

Jan Asselyn

H. 227, B. 277, Mz. 71, BB. 47-1
Etching, drypoint and burin. 218 x 170 mm.
Signed and dated: *Rembra[ndt] f. 16[. .]* (about 1647)

Jan Asselyn (1610-1652) was a Dutch painter of Italianate landscapes.

FIRST STATE

1   *National Gallery of Art, Washington, D.C. Rosenwald Collection.*

On paper with yellow fibers; perhaps of Indian origin.

The silhouette of Asselyn is reinforced by a large easel bearing a painting. The blank lower margin with its double ruled line suggests that an engraved inscription was contemplated.

Colls.: C. Ploos van Amstel; C. Josi;
Earl of Aylesford (L.58); Duke of Buccleuch (L. 402);
A. Hubert (L. 130); O. Gerstenberg; H.G. Whittemore
(L. 1384a); Lessing J. Rosenwald (L. 1760b).

SECOND STATE

The easel and painting have been scraped away and the plate burnished.

2   *Museum of Fine Arts, Boston. Harvey D. Parker Collection.*

On Japanese paper.

Traces of burnishing in combination with cloudy surface tone enliven the background. The palette and books on the table have been darkened in value by the specific application of tone.

Colls.: Earl of Aylesford (L. 58); Dukes d'Arenberg
(L. 567).

THIRD STATE

The evidence of scraping and burnishing has been completely removed. Fine hatching has been added to the edge of the cloak at lower right.

3   *Pierpont Morgan Library, New York.*

On Japanese paper.

Colls.: Richard Grenville; Harding; Lord Gosford;
H. Brodhurst (L. 1296); G.W. Vanderbilt; J. Pierpont
Morgan (L. 1509).

1. *Jan Asselyn. H. 227, first state. National Gallery of Art.*

2.   *Jan Asselyn. H. 227, second state. Museum of Fine Arts, Boston.*

2a.   Detail of Jan Asselyn. H. 227, second state. Museum of Fine Arts, Boston.

3. *Jan Asselyn. H. 227, third state. Pierpont Morgan Library.*

II

Jan Six

H. 228, B. 285, Mz. 70, BB. 47-B
Etching, drypoint and burin. 244 x 190 mm.
Signed and dated: *Rembrandt f. 1647*

Jan Six (1618-1700) was a merchant, man of letters, friend
and patron of Rembrandt.

SECOND STATE
In this state Rembrandt removed the fine shading in the
lower window which identifies the extremely rare first state.
The print is now signed and dated in the lower right margin.

4   *Pierpont Morgan Library, New York.*

On Japanese paper.

The color and luminosity of the paper give a strong
suggestion of warm sunlight entering the room.

Colls.: C. Ploos van Amstel; Heneage Finch, fifth
Earl of Aylesford (L. 58); R.S. Holford (L. 2243);
A. Hubert (L. 130); J. Pierpont Morgan (L.1509).

THIRD STATE
Jan Six's name and age (29) have been added in the lower
left margin.

5   *The Metropolitan Museum of Art, New York. Gift of
Felix M. Warburg and his Family.*

Watermark: top of crowned shield.

A very strong impression on white paper in which a
bright light picks out the many fine details of the
interior and penetrates the heavy shadows.

Colls.: Probably C. Josi (L. 2883); H.S. Theobald
(L. 1375); F.M. Warburg.

20   4.   Jan Six. H. 228, second state. Pierpont Morgan Library. Illustration reduced.

4a.   *Detail of Jan Six. H. 228, second state. Pierpont Morgan Library.*

4b.   *Detail of Jan Six. H. 228, second state. Pierpont Morgan Library.*

5. *Jan Six. H. 228, third state. The Metropolitan Museum of Art. Illustration reduced.*

III

Rembrandt Drawing at a Window

H. 229, B. 22, Mz. 26, BB. 48-A
Etching, drypoint and burin. 160 x 130 mm.
Signed and dated from II onwards: *Rembrandt f. 1648*

FIRST STATE

6 *Pierpont Morgan Library, New York.*

On European paper without watermark.

Known in only a few impressions, this state has a direct, immediate character, especially in the bold drypoint strokes which contrast so vividly with the fine web of etched lines. An incompletely burnished area of previous work appears on the papers below the artist's right hand.

Colls.: T. Worlidge, 1757; British Museum, duplicate (L. 305); R. Dighton (L. 727); H.S. Theobald; O. Gerstenberg; J.P. Morgan.

SECOND STATE

The top of the plate has been trimmed to straighten the edge. There is now a scroll in the window opening bearing the signature and date. Further work defines and models the figure and its setting.

7 *Pierpont Morgan Library, New York.*

On European paper without watermark.

The new definition given to all elements of the composition results in a sense of greater stability. The look of absorbed self scrutiny which characterized Rembrandt's expression in the first state is now less pronounced.

Colls.: A.P.F. Robert-Dumesnil; Berlin Kupferstich-kabinett, duplicate (L. 1606); G.W. Vanderbilt; J. Pierpont Morgan (L. 1509).

THIRD STATE

Parallel shading is added on the artist's right hand, his left side and on the forehead.

8 *National Gallery of Art, Washington, D.C. Rosenwald Collection.*

On European paper; no visible watermark.

Colls.: Friedrich August II (L. 972); H.E. ten Cate (L. 533b); L.J. Rosenwald (L. 1760 b-c).

FOURTH STATE

The landscape added in this state utilizes some of the lines of foul biting that occurred in the second state. The heavy reworking of the whole plate includes conspicuous drypoint lines on the jacket, and shading on the window frame and the scroll. Some authorities doubt that the work in this state is by Rembrandt.

9 *Yale University Art Gallery, New Haven. Fritz Achelis Memorial Collection.*

On European paper without watermark.

6. Rembrandt Drawing at a Window. H. 229, first state. Pierpont Morgan Library.

7. *Rembrandt Drawing at a Window. H. 229, second state. Pierpont Morgan Library.*

8.   *Rembrandt Drawing at a Window. H. 229, third state. National Gallery of Art.*

9. *Rembrandt Drawing at a Window. H. 229, fourth state. Yale University Art Gallery.*

IV

Christit with the Sick around Him, Receiving Little Children ("The Hundred Guilder Print")

H. 236, B. 74, Mz. 217, BB. 49-1
Etching, drypoint and burin. 283 x 395 mm.
Not signed or dated; completed about 1649

SECOND STATE

The change between the first and second states consists only in minor shading added to the ass's neck at right. However, stylistic differences within the composition have led some authorities to the conclusion that Rembrandt worked on the plate from about 1639 to 1649. Evidence of an earlier conception of the subject may be seen, for example, in traces of a former position of Christ's left hand.

10 *Museum of Fine Arts, Boston. Gift of Mrs. Horatio G. Curtis.*

On Japanese paper.

Virtually all fine impressions of this print are inked differently. Rembrandt's constant exploration of the different dramatic and compositional possibilities which were latent in the plate is singularly appropriate to a composition which unites various isolated incidents related in Matthew, chapter 19, into one all-embracing statement about Christ's teachings. In this impression light surface tone tempers the contrast between the lightly shaded figures at the left and the heavily worked figures at the right, some of which are picked out by delicate wiping. Christ's figure has been wiped in a manner which suggests that light emanates from His person.

Colls.: Damery (L. 2862); Calonne; W. Edwards (L. 2616); W. Esdaile (L. 2617); A. Posonyi (L. 2040-1).

11 *Boston Public Library. Wiggin Collection.*

This impression is printed on a Japanese paper very similar in color and quality to the preceding impression, but the print is completely different in effect. Relatively little surface tone has been left on the plate. The contours of Christ's figure are more heavily inked and the bitten granular tone on Christ's robe, which was almost removed by wiping in the above impression, is here very visible.

12 *The Art Institute of Chicago. The John H. Wrenn Memorial Collection.*

An impression with considerable surface tone on a Japanese paper darker than that employed for the two foregoing impressions.

Colls.: P. Remy (L. 2136); E.T. Rodenacker (L. 2438); J.H. Wrenn (L. 1475).

13 *Pierpont Morgan Library, New York.*

In this impression on a Japanese paper that is very warm in tone, the dramatic contrast between the more open areas at the left and the dense velvety shadows at the right is particularly strong. The plate has been carefully inked so that such elements of the background as the rocky promontory, which gives greater prominence to the figure of Christ, do not read too distinctly, but only partly emerge from the shadow which envelops them. This painterly handling of the background forms is characteristic of most fine impressions.

Colls.: H. Weber (L. 1383); A. Hubert (L. 130); O. Gerstenberg; M.D. (L. 1862d); E. Achelis.

14 *Pierpont Morgan Library, New York.*

Watermark: lily in shield, countermark *IV* (see Heawood 1721A).

In the foregoing impressions, the etched and drypoint lines are softened by the tonalities of the Japanese paper on which they are printed, producing a unified pictorial effect. In this brilliant impression on white paper, fine detail is unusually legible and the areas of heavy shadow especially transparent.

Colls.: Sir William Knighton; T.J. Thompson (L. 2442); C.J. Palmer; W.J. White; H. Brodhurst (L. 1296); G.W. Vanderbilt; J. Pierpont Morgan (L. 1509).

15   *The Metropolitan Museum of Art, New York. Bequest of Mrs. H.O. Havemeyer.*

Watermark: lily in shield, countermark *IV* (see Heawood 1721A).

A strong, well balanced impression on white paper.

Colls.: F. Rechberger, 1808 (L. 2133); Count Moriz von Fries; Baron J.G. Verstolk van Soelen (L. 2490); R. Fisher (L. 2204); H.O. Havemeyer.

LATE IMPRESSIONS FROM THE PLATE

16   *Museum of Fine Arts, Boston. Gift of Horatio G. Curtis.* An impression taken when the copper plate was worn down by the pressure of repeated printings.

17   *Museum of Fine Arts, Boston. Harvey D. Parker Collection.*

Captain William Baillie (1723-1810), art dealer and enthusiastic amateur of Rembrandt's etchings, who purchased the copper plate from the painter and engraver John Greenwood, extensively reworked it and about 1775 printed an edition of one hundred impressions. His attempted restoration is hard and unfeeling, lacking all the subtleties of Rembrandt's own work on the plate.

Coll.: H.F. Sewall (L. 1309).

18   *Museum of Fine Arts, Boston. Harvey D. Parker Collection.*

Baillie subsequently cut the plate into four pieces.

The impressions exhibited here are printed on a variety of papers, both European and Oriental in type. The central fragment was further reworked and the top of the plate arched.

Coll.: H.F. Sewall (L. 1309).

30   10.   *Christ with the Sick around Him. H. 236, second state. Museum of Fine Arts, Boston. Illustration reduced.*

10a. *Detail of Christ with the Sick around Him. H. 236, second state.*
Museum of Fine Arts, Boston.

11a. *Detail of Christ with the Sick around Him. H. 236, second state.*
Boston Public Library.

17a. *Detail of Christ with the Sick around Him. H. 236. Plate reworked by*
Baillie. Museum of Fine Arts, Boston.

11.   *Christ with the Sick around Him. H. 236, second state. Boston Public Library. Illustration reduced.*

12. *Christ with the Sick around Him. H. 236, second state. The Art Institute of Chicago. Illustration reduced.*

33

13.   *Christ with the Sick around Him. H. 236, second state. Pierpont Morgan Library. Illustration reduced.*

14.   *Christ with the Sick around Him. H. 236, second state. Pierpont Morgan Library. Illustration reduced.*   35

14a.   *Detail of Christ with the Sick around Him. H. 236, second state. Pierpont Morgan Library.*

14b.   *Detail of Christ with the Sick around Him. H. 236, second state. Pierpont Morgan Library.*

15. *Christ with the Sick around Him. H. 236, second state. The Metropolitan Museum of Art. Illustration reduced.*   37

16. *Christ with the Sick around Him. H. 236, late impression. Museum of Fine Arts, Boston. Illustration reduced.*

17. *Christ with the Sick around Him. H. 236. Plate reworked by Baillie.* Museum of Fine Arts, Boston. Illustration reduced.   39

18. *Christ with the Sick around Him. Plate as cut up by Baillie.*
H. 236. Museum of Fine Arts, Boston. Illustration reduced.

18a. *Christ with the Sick around Him. Central fragment further reworked by Baillie.*
H. 236. Museum of Fine Arts, Boston. Illustration reduced.

Landscape with Trees,
Farm Buildings and a Tower

H. 244, B. 223, Mz. 168, BB. 50-4
Etching and drypoint. 123 x 320 mm.
Not signed or dated; about 1650

FIRST STATE

19 *Pierpont Morgan Library, New York.*
    A clean wiped impression on Japanese paper.

    Colls.: Heneage Finch, fifth Earl of Aylesford (L. 58);
    R.S. Holford (L. 2243); A. Hubert (L. 130);
    O. Gerstenberg; J.P. Morgan.

SECOND STATE
The area of foul biting in the sky, which in the first state
printed as broad black lines, has been partially removed.

20 *Museum of Fine Arts, Boston. Harvey D. Parker
    Collection.*

    Watermark: fragment of foolscap (see Heawood 1921,
    1922, and Churchill 344).

    A relatively even surface tone covers the plate. Before
    printing, the ink was wiped from the small area of
    foul biting to the left of the large thatched roof. At
    some time, the sheet was cut at the right, probably by
    accident, and has been rejoined.

    Colls.: A. Firmin-Didot (L. 119); H.F. Sewall (L. 1309).

THIRD STATE
The cupola has been removed from the tower and the area
of foul biting in the sky completely cleaned. Additional
work in drypoint darkens the horizon at left and the large
thatched roof.

21 *Pierpont Morgan Library, New York.*
    Watermark: foolscap with five points (see Heawood
    1923).

    A light even film of ink over the entire plate creates
    a tonal effect similar to that which appears in the
    following impression, printed on Japanese paper.

    Colls.: G.W. Vanderbilt; J. Pierpont Morgan (L. 1509).

FOURTH STATE
The shadow behind the drawbridge has been deepened by
parallel lines.

22 *National Gallery of Art, Washington, D.C. Gift of
    R. Horace Gallatin.*

    On European paper; no visible watermark.

    Tone veils the plate and is particularly evident along
    the road and in front of the buildings, linking the two
    darkest elements of the composition.

    Colls.: H. Danby Seymour (L. 176); R. Horace Gallatin.

23 *The Art Institute of Chicago. The Clarence
    Buckingham Collection.*

    On European paper without watermark.

    Surface tone is used to extend the shadow cast by the
    high thatched roof.

    Colls.: M.J. Perry (L. 1880); C.J. Kollmann (L. 1584).

19. *Landscape with Trees, Farm Buildings and a Tower. H. 244, first state. Pierpont Morgan Library. Illustration reduced.*

20. *Landscape with Trees, Farm Buildings and a Tower. H. 244, second state. Museum of Fine Arts, Boston. Illustration reduced.*

43

21.   *Landscape with Trees, Farm Buildings and a Tower. H. 244, third state. Pierpont Morgan Library. Illustration reduced.*

44   22.   *Landscape with Trees, Farm Buildings and a Tower. H. 244, fourth state. National Gallery of Art. Illustration reduced.*

21a.   *Detail of Landscape with Trees, Farm Buildings and a Tower. H. 244, third state. Pierpont Morgan Library.*   45

46   23. *Landscape with Trees, Farm Buildings and a Tower. H. 244, fourth state. The Art Institute of Chicago. Illustration reduced.*

VI

Landscape with Three Gabled Cottages beside a Road

H. 246, B. 217, Mz. 163, BB. 50-D
Etching and drypoint. 162 x 203 mm.
Signed and dated: *Rembrandt f. 1650*

SECOND STATE
In this state Rembrandt shaded blank areas in the foreground with parallel lines.

24 *Museum of Fine Arts, Boston. Francis Bartlett Fund.*

On European paper without watermark.

Colls.: Friedrich August II (L. 972); GA (L. 1133a).

THIRD STATE
Diagonal hatching darkens the gable end of the first cottage.

25 *Yale University Art Gallery, New Haven. Fritz Achelis Memorial Collection.*

On European paper without watermark.

All three impressions exhibited here illustrate the variety of drypoint effects possible in fine early impressions. This is one in which the drypoint burr is unusually strong.

26 *The Metropolitan Museum of Art, New York. Bequest of Mrs. H.O. Havemeyer.*

Watermark: foolscap with five points (see Heawood 1922).

Colls.: H. Brodhurst (L. 1296); H.O. Havemeyer.

48   24.   *Landscape with Three Gabled Cottages beside a Road. H. 246, second state. Museum of Fine Arts, Boston.*

25. *Landscape with Three Gabled Cottages beside a Road. H. 246, third state. Yale University Art Gallery.* 49

26.   *Landscape with Three Gabled Cottages beside a Road. H. 246, third state. The Metropolitan Museum of Art.*

VII

The Goldweigher's Field

H. 249, B. 234, Mz. 167, BB. 51-A
Etching and drypoint. 118 x 320 mm.
Signed and dated: *Rembrandt 1651*

ONLY STATE

27 *The Art Institute of Chicago. The Clarence Buckingham Collection.*

In this superb impression the absorbent Japanese paper not only causes the drypoint burr to register more strongly, but serves, together with a film of light surface ink, as an intermediate tone which unites these scattered drypoint accents.

Colls.: J. Barnard (L. 1419); G. Hibbert (L. 2849); R.S. Holford (L. 2243); H.S. Theobald (L. 1375); O. Gerstenberg (L. 2785); H.G. Whittemore (L. 1384a).

28 *Pierpont Morgan Library, New York.*
Watermark: lily in shield (see Heawood 1730).

Another fine impression in which the drypoint accents are strong. Vertical polishing marks and accidental tone resulting from false biting lend color to the sky.

Colls.: G.W. Vanderbilt; J. Pierpont Morgan (L. 1509).

29 *The Metropolitan Museum of Art, New York. Jacob H. Schiff Fund and Edwin D. Levinson Gift.*

Watermark: fragment, top of crown above pascal lamb (see Heawood 2842).

A fine, even impression in which, because the drypoint accents are less strong, the feeling of depth in the landscape is more convincing.

Colls.: P. Mariette, 1672; A. Morrison? (L. 144).

30 *National Gallery of Art, Washington, D.C. Rosenwald Collection.*

On European paper; no visible watermark.

This is one of some half-dozen surviving counterproofs of this landscape. It has been suggested that the relative frequency of counterproofs of this subject may be explained by the fact that they represent accurately the view toward Haarlem, whereas impressions from the plate show a reversed image.

Colls.: A. Artaria (L. 33); Marquis B. de Florence; C. Delanglade (L. 660); G.W. Nowell-Usticke.

27.   *The Goldweigher's Field. H. 249, only state. The Art Institute of Chicago. Illustration reduced.*

27a.   *Detail of The Goldweigher's Field. H. 249, only state. The Art Institute of Chicago. Illustration reduced.*

28.   *The Goldweigher's Field. H. 249, only state. Pierpont Morgan Library. Illustration reduced.*

29. *The Goldweigher's Field. H. 249, only state. The Metropolitan Museum of Art. Illustration reduced.*

30. *The Goldweigher's Field. H. 249, only state. Counterproof. National Gallery of Art. Illustration reduced.*

VIII

Clement de Jonghe

H. 251, B. 272, Mz. 72, BB. 51-C
Etching, drypoint and burin. 207 x 162 mm.
Signed and dated: *Rembrandt f. 1651*

Clement de Jonghe was active as a printseller and publisher in Amsterdam from about 1640 until his death in 1679. The inventory of his estate provides the first extensive listing of Rembrandt's etchings.

FIRST STATE. Etching only.

31   *Pierpont Morgan Library, New York.*

On European paper without watermark.

This initial statement seems to be a straightforward record of the sitter's physiognomy and costume, but does not comment on his inner character. Lines of abrasion resulting from the polishing of the plate print as a tonal effect very similar to surface tone.

Colls.: G.W. Vanderbilt; J. Pierpont Morgan (L. 1509).

32   *Pierpont Morgan Library, New York.*

On Japanese paper.

Impressions of this print on Japanese paper are rare. Since the image is too light in tonality to print effectively on this darker paper, Rembrandt may have preferred the daylight effect of the first state when printed on white paper.

Colls.: Cambridge University Library, duplicate (L. 2475); E.T. Rodenacker (L. 2438); H.S. Theobald (L. 1375); J. Pierpont Morgan (L. 1509).

SECOND STATE
Drypoint and burin shading have been added to the hat, face, cloak and the chair at the right. The iris of the sitter's right eye has been enlarged. His mouth, particularly the fleshy upper lip, has been more clearly defined.

33   *Pierpont Morgan Library, New York.*

Watermark: pascal lamb (see Heawood 2842).

Although Clement de Jonghe's features are more strongly modelled by shading, the cast shadow of the hat brim tends to obscure them.

THIRD STATE
The shape of the hat has been made more regular and a hatband added. Additional work casts the right side of the sitter's features into deeper shadow. A framing arch has been sketchily indicated in drypoint.

34   *Museum of Fine Arts, Boston. William Francis Warden Fund.*

Watermark: pascal lamb with *4* above *WR* (see Heawood 2843).

The shadowing of the sitter's face, already very evident in the second state, has been intensified, with the result that it is difficult to discern his features or to define the expression which they convey. The irregular play of reflected light over the darkened features further heightens the ambiguity. The simplification of the rumpled hat of the first state into an ideally regular shape parallels the transformation of the portrait of an individual into a more generalized human image.

Colls.: S. Kalmann; R. Ritter von Gutmann (L. 2770).

FOURTH STATE
The folds and contours of the costume have been reworked to give the sitter's body new weight and solidity. The arch shape has been elaborated in etching and now reads as a niche in the background wall where texture is further suggested by the accidental effects of rebiting.

35   *Pierpont Morgan Library, New York.*

On European paper without watermark.

Whereas in the third state all attention was focused on the head, the body now assumes equal importance.

Colls.: T. Irwin (L. 1540); J. Pierpont Morgan (L. 1509).

FIFTH STATE
The triangular section of the chairback has been burnished out, as well as an area to the left of the sitter's hair. Some authorities doubt that the work in this state is by Rembrandt.

36   *Museum of Fine Arts, Boston. Harvey D. Parker Collection.*

On European paper without watermark.

Coll.: H.F. Sewall (L. 1309).

31. *Clement de Jonghe. H. 251, first state. Pierpont Morgan Library.*

32.   Clement de Jonghe. H. 251, first state. Pierpont Morgan Library.

33. *Clement de Jonghe. H. 251, second state. Pierpont Morgan Library.*

34. *Clement de Jonghe. H. 251, third state. Museum of Fine Arts, Boston.*   59

35. *Clement de Jonghe. H. 251, fourth state. Pierpont Morgan Library.*

36. *Clement de Jonghe. H. 251, fifth state. Museum of Fine Arts, Boston.*

The Adoration of the Shepherds: A Night Piece

H. 255, B. 46, Mz. 237, BB. 52-1
Etching, drypoint and burin. 152 x 198 mm.
Not signed or dated; about 1652

In the first state of this print, there is a strong source of light on the right behind Joseph, which illuminates the Virgin and Child and the sheaves behind them. In the successive states Rembrandt shaded the background, the bedding and the faces of the Holy Family, thus darkening the right side of the composition.

FOURTH STATE

37 *Pierpont Morgan Library, New York.*

On Japanese paper.

A clean wiped impression in which the fine mesh of lines evokes a darkened stable interior lit from two sources: the light of the lantern, which is reflected in the faces of the shepherds, and a hidden source of light which silhouettes Joseph and reveals the Mother and Child.

Colls.: J.-L.-H. Le Secq, called Des Tournelles (L. 1336); O. Gerstenberg; J.P. Morgan.

38 *Museum of Fine Arts, Boston. Harvey D. Parker Collection.*

Watermark: fragment, *4 over WR*

In this impression some surface tone has been left in the background to give greater emphasis to the darkness beyond the narrow circle of light about the Holy Family.

Colls.: F. Rechberger (L. 2133); H.F. Sewall (L. 1309).

FIFTH STATE

A partition of horizontal planks has been added behind Joseph's head. His hat is given texture with short burin strokes. The sheaves are reworked in drypoint and appear as a dark corona behind the Virgin and Child. The faces of the shepherds and the area of background behind the lantern have been lightened by burnishing.

39 *National Gallery of Art, Washington, D.C. Rosenwald Collection.*

A luminous impression on Japanese paper in which details are very legible.

Colls.: J.C. de Pomal (L. 429); A. Artaria (L. 33); L.J. Rosenwald (L. 1760b).

SIXTH STATE

Curved lines of drypoint have been added to the pillow above the Infant's head.

40 *Pierpont Morgan Library, New York.*

On European paper without watermark.

A very warm, rich impression.

Colls.: J.-L.-H. Le Secq, called Des Tournelles (L. 1336); O. Gerstenberg; J.P. Morgan.

SEVENTH STATE

The planks behind Joseph's head have been lightened by burnishing.

41 *Pierpont Morgan Library, New York.*

On European paper without watermark.

In this impression the deeply engraved lines normally obscured by plate tone may be seen, particularly in the foreground.

Colls.: Count G. Archinto (L. 547); T. Irwin (L. 1540); J. Pierpont Morgan (L. 1509).

42 *Museum of Fine Arts, Boston. Special Print Fund, 1894.*

On European paper without watermark.

Tone on the plate gives the effect of an earlier state, even though most of the drypoint burr has disappeared.

Coll.: J. Peoli (L. 2020).

37. *The Adoration of the Shepherds: A Night Piece. H. 255, fourth state. Pierpont Morgan Library.*

38.   *The Adoration of the Shepherds: A Night Piece. H. 255, fourth state. Museum of Fine Arts, Boston.*

39. *The Adoration of the Shepherds: A Night Piece. H. 255, fifth state. National Gallery of Art.*   65

39a.   *Detail of* The Adoration of the Shepherds: A Night Piece. *H. 255, fifth state.*
       National Gallery of Art.

40.   *The Adoration of the Shepherds: A Night Piece. H. 255, sixth state. Pierpont Morgan Library.*

41. *The Adoration of the Shepherds: A Night Piece. H. 255, seventh state. Pierpont Morgan Library.*

42.   *The Adoration of the Shepherds: A Night Piece. H. 255, seventh state. Museum of Fine Arts, Boston.*   69

X

Christ Preaching ("La Petite Tombe")

H. 256, B. 67, Mz. 236, BB. 52-2
Etching, drypoint and burin. 156 x 206 mm.
Not signed or dated; about 1652

ONLY STATE

43 *Museum of Fine Arts, Boston. Gift of William Norton Bullard.*

On European paper without watermark.

A strong impression on white paper which emphasizes the structural clarity with which figures and setting have been related.

Coll.: F. Bullard (L. 982).

44 *Pierpont Morgan Library, New York.*

An impression on Japanese paper which is in sharp contrast to the above impression in its blurred contours and opaque areas of deep shadow. These effects are attributable in part to the manner in which heavy drypoint burr prints on the absorbent Japanese paper. Deep shadow obscures the people behind Christ and emphasizes his figure. In this impression the artist seems to have attempted to change the old man at the right margin from a seated to a standing figure by means of special inking.

Colls.: J. Barnard (L. 1419); W. Esdaile (L. 2617); H. Brodhurst (L. 1296); G.W. Vanderbilt; J. Pierpont Morgan (L. 1509).

45 *Private Collection*

Another impression on Japanese paper in which light surface tone is visible on the front of the platform on which Christ stands and in which there is an especially satisfying balance between sharply defined lines and soft masses of drypoint.

Coll.: Leonard Gow.

43. *Christ Preaching. H. 256, only state. Museum of Fine Arts, Boston.*

44. *Christ Preaching. H. 256, only state. Pierpont Morgan Library.*

45.   *Christ Preaching. H. 256, only state. Private Collection.*   73

XI

Faust in His Study, Watching a Magic Disk

H. 260, B. 270, Mz. 275, BB. 52-4.
Etching, drypoint and burin. 209 x 160 mm.
Not signed or dated; about 1652

FIRST STATE

46   *Pierpont Morgan Library, New York.*

Watermark: quartered shield, unidentified.

An early impression where the drypoint burr is strong and especially prominent on Faust's robe, the curtain at left, and in the modelling of the skull. A ghostly film of tone covers the magic disk and its rays, suggesting that the vision exists on a plane apart from the brilliant light of the clean wiped window.

47   *Museum of Fine Arts, Boston. Gift of Miss Ellen Bullard.*

On oatmeal (cartridge) paper.

The plate has been wiped very clean before printing, with the result that the books and papers on the shelves of the left background are more easily seen. The texture and tonality of the grayish oatmeal paper help to convey the atmosphere of a dim and dusty study.

Colls.: J. Reiss (L. 1522); A. Hubert (L. 130).

SECOND STATE

Extremely fine parallel lines which give the effect of drypoint are used to shade Faust's robe, particularly on the shoulders and lapels, as well as the pile of books on the right. Vertical strokes have been added to the third windowpane down, on the extreme right.

48   *Pierpont Morgan Library, New York.*

Watermark: large lily in crowned shield (see Heawood 1784).

From the second state onwards, retouching seems to have been a frequent necessity. The hand holding the disk is an example of fresh drypoint work.

Colls.: A.N. Alferoff (L. 1727); T. Irwin (L. 1540); J. Pierpont Morgan (L. 1509).

INTERMEDIATE STATE
BETWEEN SECOND AND THIRD

The deep, narrow folds on the left lapel of the robe have been further extended by fine shading. Diagonal shading has been added to the ledge below the skull where formerly the lines were only vertical and horizontal.

49   *The Art Institute of Chicago. The Clarence Buckingham Collection.*

On Japanese paper.

There are impressions on white paper in the Pierpont Morgan Library, The Metropolitan Museum of Art and the Museum of Fine Arts, Boston, which show precisely the same stage of work on the plate.

Colls.: J. Barnard (L. 1419); G. Hibbert (L. 2849); Earl of Aylesford (L. 58); A. Morrison (L. 151).

THIRD STATE

Strong parallel lines have been added to the pile of books at the right. The shading on the lapel has been extended to its full length and the outline of the shoulder strengthened. Additional rework is visible throughout, darkening the background.

50   *Pierpont Morgan Library, New York.*

On European paper without watermark.

46. *Faust in His Study, Watching a Magic Disk. H. 260, first state. Pierpont Morgan Library.*

46a.   *Detail of Faust in His Study, Watching a Magic Disk. H. 260, first state. Pierpont Morgan Library.*

46b.   *Detail of Faust in His Study, Watching a Magic Disk. H. 260, first state. Pierpont Morgan Library.*

47. *Faust in His Study, Watching a Magic Disk. H. 260, first state. Museum of Fine Arts, Boston.*

48. *Faust in His Study, Watching a Magic Disk. H. 260, second state. Pierpont Morgan Library.*

49. *Faust in His Study, Watching a Magic Disk. H. 260, intermediate state between second and third.*
   The Art Institute of Chicago.

50.   *Faust in His Study, Watching a Magic Disk. H. 260, third state. Pierpont Morgan Library.*

XII

Saint Jerome Reading in an Italian Landscape

H. 267, B. 104, Mz. 249, BB. 53-3
Etching, drypoint and burin. 260 x 207 mm.
Not signed or dated; about 1653-54

FIRST STATE

51 *Pierpont Morgan Library, New York.*
    The warm tonality of the Japanese paper of this
    impression suggests a landscape radiant with sunlight.
    Careful wiping of the hillside in the distance not only
    reinforces this effect, but also provides a sharper con-
    trast to the exceptionally dark drypoint burr on the lion
    and the vegetation of the foreground, thus creating a
    greater illusion of depth. The horizontal lines of
    abrasion resulting from the polishing of the plate have
    been retained for their tonal effect.

    Colls.: H. Brodhurst (L. 1296); G.W. Vanderbilt;
    J. Pierpont Morgan (L. 1509).

SECOND STATE

The supports of the bridge have been strengthened with
drypoint.

52 *Museum of Fine Arts, Boston. Harvey D. Parker
    Collection.*

    One of a few impressions of the second state printed on
    oatmeal (cartridge) paper. This gray-brown European
    paper, like the darker shades of Japanese paper, offers a
    middle range of values which mutes sharp contrasts in
    the same manner as the etcher's use of light surface
    tone on other occasions.

    Colls.: Cabinet Brentano-Birckenstock (L. 345);
    M. Holloway (L. 1875); H.F. Sewall (L. 1309).

53 *The Art Institute of Chicago. The Clarence
    Buckingham Collection.*

    Watermark: Strasburg bend (see Churchill 268).

    A fine impression on white paper.

    Coll.: Cabinet of the Princes of Waldburg Wolfegg,
    duplicate (L. 2542).

51. Saint Jerome Reading in an Italian Landscape. H. 267, first state. Pierpont Morgan Library. Illustration reduced.

51a.   Detail of Saint Jerome Reading in an Italian Landscape. H. 267, first state. Pierpont Morgan Library.

84   52.   *Saint Jerome Reading in an Italian Landscape. H. 267, second state. Museum of Fine Arts, Boston. Illustration reduced.*

53. *Saint Jerome Reading in an Italian Landscape. H. 267, second state. The Art Institute of Chicago. Illustration reduced.*   85

XIII

Christ Crucified between the Two Thieves: Large Oblong Plate ("The Three Crosses")

H. 270, B. 78, Mz. 223, BB. 53-A
Drypoint and burin. 385 x 450 mm.
Signed and dated in III only: *Rembrandt f. 1653*

FIRST STATE
The plate is executed entirely in drypoint and burin.

54   *Pierpont Morgan Library, New York.*

Watermark: Strasburg bend in shield surmounted by lily (see Heawood 63).

In this impression some surface tone has been left along the foreground and at the sides so as to reinforce the effect of a central shaft of light.

Colls.: C.H. Watelet; Baron D. Vivant Denon; J.H. Hawkins; J. Sheepshanks; J.W. Wilson; Walter Francis, fifth Duke of Buccleuch (L. 402); T. Irwin (L. 1540); J. Pierpont Morgan (L. 1509).

55   *National Gallery of Art, Washington, D.C. Gift of R. Horace Gallatin.*

On vellum.

There are a number of impressions of this state on vellum. On this very absorbent surface the ink spreads, softening the lines, and where there is heavy drypoint burr creating broad areas of opaque shadow. In this impression substantial surface tone contributes to the effect of general darkness anticipating the mood of the fourth state.

Coll.: R. Horace Gallatin.

SECOND STATE
The figure at the right margin has been darkened by shading.

56   *Pierpont Morgan Library, New York.*

Watermark: Strasburg bend in shield surmounted by lily (see Heawood 63).

The use of surface tone in this impression is very comparable to that in the first state belonging to the Morgan Library.

Colls.: H. Brodhurst (L. 1296); G.W. Vanderbilt; J. Pierpont Morgan (L. 1509).

57   *The Metropolitan Museum of Art, New York. Gift of Felix M. Warburg and his Family.*

On vellum.

Coll.: F.M. Warburg.

THIRD STATE
Additional work darkens the crowd at left and the foreground. The figure at the right margin is nearly obscured by further shading. The plate is signed and dated.

58   *Private Collection.*

Watermark: Strasburg bend in shield surmounted by lily (see Heawood 63).

A fine impression, characteristic of this state in that it is printed on white paper with relatively little surface tone.

Coll.: Albertina, Vienna, duplicate (L. 174).

FOURTH STATE
Rembrandt has completely revised the plate. He has removed much previous work by means of scraping and burnishing, especially on the left side of the composition where new figures replace those which were eliminated. The group of mourners at the right remains, but it has been radically altered in conception. The plate has been darkened overall by powerful parallel strokes of the drypoint and burin. As opposed to the variety of dramatic incident which attracted the eye in the first three states, the figure of Christ is now the central point of focus. Recent stylistic comparisons by authorities suggest that this state was executed about 1660-1661.

59   *National Gallery of Art, Washington, D.C. Rosenwald Collection.*

On European paper.

Impressions of this state vary according to the amount

of drypoint burr that is visible and the amount of ink left on the plate. The present impression is one of a number, heavily inked and with surface tone, which reinforces the image of "darkness over all the land" (Matt. 27:45).

Colls.: W. Esdaile (L. 2617); A. Morrison ? (L. 144); L.J. Rosenwald (L. 1760b).

60 *Library of Congress, Washington, D.C., Prints and Photographs Division.*

On Japanese paper.

An impression with surface tone and unusually rich in drypoint.

Coll.: Gardiner Greene Hubbard Collection, Washington, D.C. (L. 1267b).

61 *The Art Institute of Chicago. The Clarence Buckingham Collection.*

Watermark: unidentified coat-of-arms.

In this impression one can read quite clearly the images from previous states which Rembrandt did not completely remove from the plate. The ghostly outlines of these half-obliterated figures persist and contribute to the impression of chaos.

62 *Museum of Fine Arts, Boston. Harvey D. Parker Collection.*

On European paper without watermark.

A fine impression in which there is a satisfying balance between concealing darkness and legibility.

Colls.: Walter Francis, fifth Duke of Buccleuch (L. 402); H.S. Theobald (L. 1375).

63 *Pierpont Morgan Library, New York.*

On European paper without watermark.

Relatively little surface tone has been employed on the left side of the plate, exposing a surprisingly spare network of lines and disturbing the sense of compositional balance. This example reveals how important surface ink is for the success of impressions of this state.

Colls.: K.E. von Liphart (L. 1687); G.W. Vanderbilt; J. Pierpont Morgan (L. 1509).

54.   *Christ Crucified between the Two Thieves. H. 270, first state. Pierpont Morgan Library. Illustration reduced.*

55. *Christ Crucified between the Two Thieves. H. 270, first state. National Gallery of Art. Illustration reduced.*

56. *Christ Crucified between the Two Thieves. H. 270, second state. Pierpont Morgan Library. Illustration reduced.*

57.   *Christ Crucified between the Two Thieves. H. 270, second state. The Metropolitan Museum of Art. Illustration reduced.*   91

58. *Christ Crucified between the Two Thieves. H. 270, third state. Private Collection. Illustration reduced.*

58a. *Detail of Christ Crucified between the Two Thieves. H. 270. third state. Private Collection.*

62a. *Detail of Christ Crucified between the Two Thieves. H. 270, fourth state. Museum of Fine Arts, Boston.*

58b. *Detail of Christ Crucified between the Two Thieves. H. 270, third state. Private Collection.*

62b. *Detail of Christ Crucified between the Two Thieves. H. 270, fourth state. Museum of Fine Arts, Boston.*

58c.   *Detail of Christ Crucified between the Two Thieves. H. 270, third state. Private Collection.*

62c.   *Detail of Christ Crucified between the Two Thieves. H. 270, fourth state. Museum of Fine Arts, Boston.*   95

59.   *Christ Crucified between the Two Thieves. H. 270, fourth state. National Gallery of Art. Illustration reduced.*

60. *Christ Crucified between the Two Thieves. H. 270, fourth state. Library of Congress. Illustration reduced.* 97

61.   *Christ Crucified between the Two Thieves. H. 270, fourth state. The Art Institute of Chicago. Illustration reduced.*

62.　*Christ Crucified between the Two Thieves. H. 270, fourth state. Museum of Fine Arts, Boston. Illustration reduced.*　　99

63. *Christ Crucified between the Two Thieves. H. 270, fourth state. Pierpont Morgan Library. Illustration reduced.*

XIV

Christ Presented to the People: Large Oblong Plate ("Ecce Homo")

H. 271, B. 76, Mz. 235, BB. 55-A
Drypoint. I, II: 383 x 455 mm. III onwards: 358 x 455 mm.
Signed and dated from VI onwards: *Rembrandt f. 1655*

FIRST STATE
All states of this print are executed entirely in drypoint.

64 *Pierpont Morgan Library, New York.*

On Japanese paper.

Before printing, a strip was added at the top to enlarge the sheet. This piecing was probably necessitated by the fact that most of the sheets of Japanese paper available to Rembrandt were not large enough to accommodate the plate before it was cut down. There exist, however, two impressions printed from the uncut plate on Japanese paper which has not been pieced: an impression of the intermediate state in Vienna and an impression of the second state in London. In this impression the drypoint burr is particularly strong. Evidence of an earlier conception of the architecture may be seen at upper left.

Colls.: J.H. Hawkins; Walter Francis, fifth Duke of Buccleuch (L. 402); G.W. Vanderbilt; J. Pierpont Morgan (L. 1509).

INTERMEDIATE STATE
First described by Münz on the basis of two impressions in the Albertina, Vienna.

With additional shading which darkens the doorway on the left, but before the cross-hatching on the thigh of the man at the left of the tribune which characterizes the second state.

65 *The Metropolitan Museum of Art, New York. Gift of Felix M. Warburg and his Family.*

On Japanese paper which has been pieced at the top before printing as in the preceding impression. The drypoint burr prints less strongly, making for greater legibility. The darkening of the doorway serves to project the tribunal and its protagonists forward. There is surface tone on the foreground and on the crowd which by its contrast with the blank white base of the tribunal seems to set the mob farther apart from the figure of Christ.

Colls.: J. Barnard (L. 219); △ (Unidentified collector's mark); F.M. Warburg.

THIRD STATE
The plate has been cut at the top reducing the height by about 25 mm. A balustrade and further shading have been added to the projecting wing at the right. The legs of the man at the top of the steps at the right have been lengthened. Additional shading is seen on the rear wall of the tribunal and its occupants, and on the mound of earth in the lower left.

66 *The Metropolitan Museum of Art, New York. Gift of Felix M. Warburg and his Family.*

On Japanese paper.

The frequent choice of this paper for the printing of the plate can probably be explained by its responsiveness to the drypoint medium. The reduction of the height of the plate helps to concentrate attention on the central scene.

Colls.: F. Rechberger; F.M. Warburg.

FOURTH STATE
Vertical shading has been added in the window openings at upper right.

67 *National Gallery of Art, Washington, D.C. Rosenwald Collection.*

On European paper without watermark.

The picturesque crowd before the tribunal was removed in the fifth state. Most of the figures which remained were redrawn in drypoint in the fifth and sixth states and some figures added. Numerous alterations were made in the architecture. A sculpture of a bearded Neptune-like figure flanked by two arches was added at the base of the tribunal in the sixth state, and the plate signed and dated.

SEVENTH STATE
The Neptune-like figure in the foreground is half-obscured by horizontal shading.

68 *Pierpont Morgan Library, New York.*

Watermark: lily in shield with *IHS* (see Heawood 1780).

The roughening·of the surface of the plate which occurred when the crowd was erased is used to characterize the wall surface. Two dark archways, possibly entrances to cells or dungeons, penetrate this wall. The dimly seen, enigmatic bearded figure adds a sense of disquiet. Set off by deeper shadow and further modelled, the figure of Christ is more readily isolated from the surrounding group.

Colls.: J.H. Hawkins; Walter Francis, fifth Duke of Buccleuch (L. 402); G.W. Vanderbilt; J. Pierpont Morgan. (L. 1509).

69 *The Art Institute of Chicago. The Clarence Buckingham Collection.*

Watermark: bunch of grapes (see Heawood 2227).

64. *Christ Presented to the People. H. 271, first state. Pierpont Morgan Library. Illustration reduced.*

65.   *Christ Presented to the People. H. 271, intermediate state. The Metropolitan Museum of Art. Illustration reduced.*

65a. *Detail of Christ Presented to the People. H. 271, intermediate state. The Metropolitan Museum of Art.*

69a. *Detail of Christ Presented to the People. H. 271, seventh state. The Art Institute of Chicago.*

65b. *Detail of Christ Presented to the People. H. 271, intermediate state. The Metropolitan Museum of Art.*

69b. *Detail of Christ Presented to the People. H. 271, seventh state. The Art Institute of Chicago.*

65c.   *Detail of Christ Presented to the People. H. 271, intermediate state. The Metropolitan Museum of Art.*

69c.   *Detail of Christ Presented to the People. H. 271, seventh state. The Art Institute of Chicago.*

66.   *Christ Presented to the People. H. 271, third state. The Metropolitan Museum of Art. Illustration reduced.*

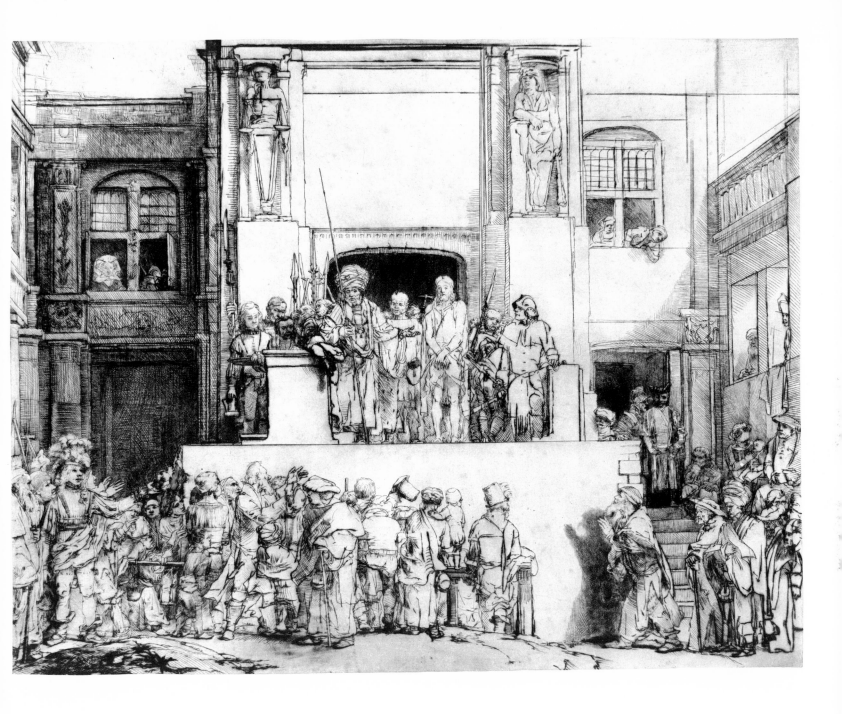

67. *Christ Presented to the People. H. 271, fourth state. National Gallery of Art. Illustration reduced.*

68. *Christ Presented to the People. H. 271, seventh state. Pierpont Morgan Library. Illustration reduced.*

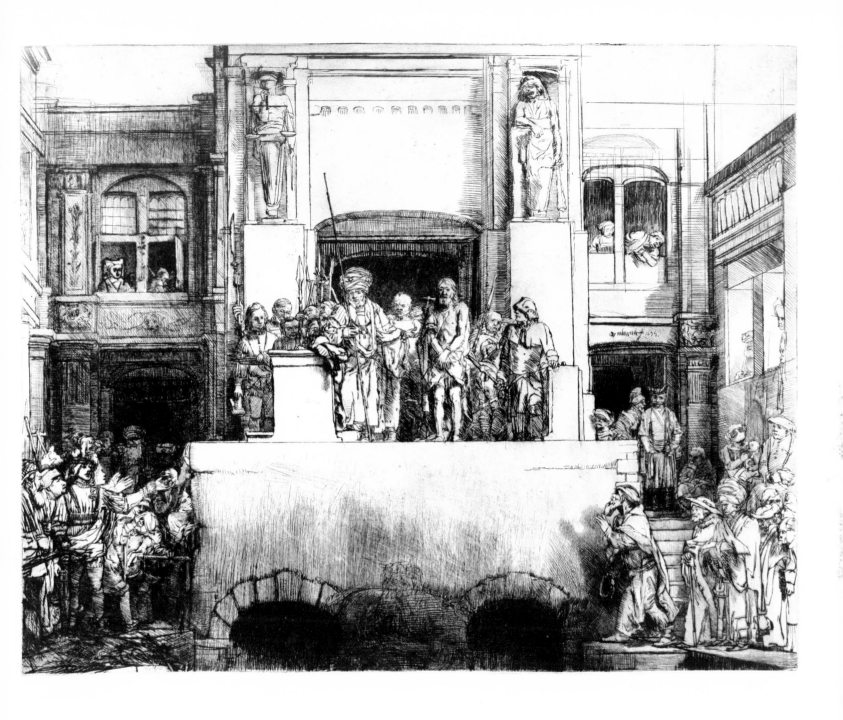

69.   *Christ Presented to the People. H. 271, seventh state. The Art Institute of Chicago. Illustration reduced.*

XV

The Adoration of the Shepherds: with the Lamp

H. 273, B. 45, Mz. 226, BB. 54-1
Etching. 105 x 130 mm.
Signed: *Rembrandt f.*, about 1654.

FIRST STATE

70   *Museum of Fine Arts, Boston. Gift of William Norton Bullard.*

On European paper without watermark.

A clean wiped impression.

Coll.: T. Dows (L. 2427).

71   *Private Collection*

On European paper; no visible watermark.

A relatively even film of tone covers the entire sheet, reducing the light of the lamp to a muted glow.

Colls.: A.N. Alferoff (L. 1727); F. Kalle (L. 1021); C. Schlösser (L. 636); E. Smith, Jr. (L. 2897); P. Davidsohn (L. 654); G.W. Nowell-Usticke.

72   *Museum of Fine Arts, Boston. Stephen Bullard Memorial Fund.*

On European paper without watermark.

An uneven film of ink covers the sheet except around the central group where a glow of light is produced by an area of circular wiping. The dim wavering light in this impression is not only more appropriate to the source, the single oil lamp, but also suggests the mystery and significance of the event.

SECOND STATE
The blank, unbitten streak at upper right is filled in with fine hatching.

73   *Museum of Fine Arts, Boston. Harvey D. Parker Collection.*

On European paper without watermark.

Coll.: H.F. Sewall (L. 1309).

70. *The Adoration of the Shepherds: with the Lamp. H. 273, first state. Museum of Fine Arts, Boston.*   *113*

71. *The Adoration of the Shepherds: with the Lamp. H. 273, first state. Private Collection.*

72. *The Adoration of the Shepherds: with the Lamp. H. 273, first state. Museum of Fine Arts, Boston.*

73.   *The Adoration of the Shepherds: with the Lamp. H. 273, second state. Museum of Fine Arts, Boston.*

XVI

The Circumcision in the Stable

H. 274, B. 47, Mz. 227, BB. 54-B
Etching. 95 x 144 mm.
Signed and dated: *Rembrandt f. 1654*

SECOND STATE
There is a blank area at the upper margin near the center.
(Recent cataloguers believe that Hind's first and second states
are identical.)

74 *Private Collection.*

On European paper; no visible watermark.

Unusually heavy surface tone covers the entire plate
except where very localized wiping picks out the participants as if spotlighted by the slanting beams of
light indicated in the etched design. The right portion
of this impression with its concealing veil of surface
tone and parallel etched lines brings to mind the
handling of certain impressions of the fourth state
of *The Three Crosses* (Cat. No. 59).

Colls.: J.D. Böhm (L. 271, 1442); G.W. Nowell-Usticke.

THIRD STATE
The blank area at the upper margin is filled in with shading.

75 *Museum of Fine Arts, Boston. Harvey D. Parker
Collection.*

Watermark: *AG*

A clean wiped impression.

Coll.: H.F. Sewall (L. 1309).

74. *The Circumcision in the Stable. H. 274, second state. Private Collection.*

75. *The Circumcision in the Stable. H. 274, third state. Museum of Fine Arts, Boston.*

XVII

The Presentation in the Temple: in the Dark Manner

H. 279, B. 50, Mz. 240, BB. 57-B
Etching, drypoint and burin. 210 x 162 mm.
Not signed or dated; about 1654 (Hind and White); about
1657 (Biörklund and Barnard).

ONLY STATE

76 *The Art Institute of Chicago. The Clarence
Buckingham Collection.*

Watermark: foolscap.

A beautiful, clean wiped impression on white paper
which reveals the homogeneous blend of techniques
(etching, drypoint, burin work, burnishing) in which
this print is executed.

Colls.: J.H. Hawkins (L. 1471); W.E. Drugulin (L. 2612);
Georg Ráth (L. 1206); B.N. Tchitcherine.

77 *Pierpont Morgan Library, New York.*

In this superb impression on Japanese paper, surface
tone and selective wiping have been used to focus
attention on Simeon, who holds the infant Christ,
and on the seated figure of the High Priest, while
subordinating the figures of Christ's parents and all
elements of the background except a mysterious
glimmer of light from the curtained window. This is
one of only five known impressions (the others to
be found in Amsterdam, Haarlem, London and Paris)
in which heavy surface tone is used to darken the
scene and vary the relationship between the
participants.

Colls.: Sir E. Astley (L. 2775); J.H. Hawkins; Walter
Francis, fifth Duke of Buccleuch (L. 402); G.W.
Vanderbilt; J. Pierpont Morgan (L. 1509).

76.   *The Presentation in the Temple. H. 279, only state. The Art Institute of Chicago.*

77. *The Presentation in the Temple. H. 279, only state. Pierpont Morgan Library.*

77a.   *Detail of* The Presentation in the Temple. *H. 279, only state. Pierpont Morgan Library.*

The Entombment

H.281, B. 86, Mz. 241, BB. 54-2
Etching, drypoint and burin. 211 x 161 mm.
Not signed or dated; about 1654

FIRST STATE

78 *Pierpont Morgan Library, New York.*

On Japanese paper.

Executed almost entirely in etching with only a few supplementary touches of drypoint on the Virgin's left elbow and the adjacent wall, the image is constructed from a transparent network of parallel lines. The strong effect of light thrown off by an artificial source shielded from our view is abetted here by the glossy white of the thin Japanese paper.

Colls.: G.W. Vanderbilt; J. Pierpont Morgan (L.1509).

SECOND STATE
The entire image has been darkened by extensive reworking of the plate.

79 *Museum of Fine Arts, Boston. Gift of William Norton Bullard.*

Watermark: foolscap (see Churchill 337).

Most impressions of the second, third and fourth states are characterized by the generous use of surface tone to modulate the light within the tomb. In this very dark impression only a feeble light, picked out by wiping, flickers over the body of the Savior.

Colls.: E.P. Otto; W. Koller, 1852 (L. 1583); F. Bullard (L. 982).

80 *The Metropolitan Museum of Art, New York. Gift of Henry Walters.*

On European paper without watermark.

An even darker impression with heavy tone covering the entire plate.

81 *Private Collection.*
A relatively clean wiped impression on yellowish vellum in which the color of the vellum vividly suggests light from a lamp or candle.

Colls.: E. Rudge; E.R. Johnson; G.W. Nowell-Usticke.

THIRD STATE
A light semicircle has been burnished behind the skulls, throwing them into relief. Diagonal shading darkens the block projecting from the right margin.

82 *Pierpont Morgan Library, New York.*

Watermark: *WK*

Heavy plate tone almost swallows up the figures at the left while wiping focuses a strong light on the body of Christ.

Colls.: A. Firmin-Didot (L. 119); T. Irwin (L. 1540); J. Pierpont Morgan (L. 1509).

83 *Private Collection.*

On European paper; no visible watermark.

Very light wiping of a film of tone draws attention to Christ and to the figures around him. The concealed light illuminating various participants in other impressions is here extinguished.

FOURTH STATE
Further diagonal shading added to the projecting block.

84 *Museum of Fine Arts, Boston. Gift of Miss Ellen Bullard.*

On European paper without watermark.

An impression which clearly shows the configuration of light and shadow which the work in the plate produces when printed without heavy surface tone.

Colls.: A.J. Lamme (L. 138); F. Bullard (L. 982).

85 *Pierpont Morgan Library, New York.*

Watermark: foolscap with seven points (see Heawood 2004, Churchill 346).

An impression with slight surface tone.

Coll.: F. Debois, 1837 (L. 985).

86   *Pierpont Morgan Library, New York.*

Watermark: foolscap with seven points (see Heawood 2004, Churchill 346).

A somber impression with heavy plate tone in which wiping illuminates not only certain figures in the group around Christ's body, but also a portion of the wall behind them. The body of Christ is shadowed by plate tone.

Colls.: Naudet (L. 1938); R.S. Holford; O. Gerstenberg; J.P. Morgan.

78.   *The Entombment. H. 281, first state. Pierpont Morgan Library.*

78a.   Detail of The Entombment. H. 281, first state. Pierpont Morgan Library.

84a. *Detail of The Entombment. H. 281, fourth state. Museum of Fine Arts, Boston.*

86a. *Detail of The Entombment. H. 281, fourth state. Pierpont Morgan Library.*

79.   *The Entombment. H. 281, second state. Museum of Fine Arts, Boston.*

80.   *The Entombment. H. 281, second state. The Metropolitan Museum of Art.*   129

81.   *The Entombment. H. 281, second state. Private Collection.*

82.   *The Entombment. H. 281, third state. Pierpont Morgan Library.*

83.   *The Entombment. H. 281, third state. Private Collection.*

84.   *The Entombment. H. 281, fourth state. Museum of Fine Arts, Boston.*   133

85.   *The Entombment. H. 281, fourth state. Pierpont Morgan Library.*

86. *The Entombment. H. 281, fourth state. Pierpont Morgan Library.*

XIX

Christ at Emmaus: The Larger Plate

H. 282, B. 87, Mz. 233, BB. 54-H.
Etching, burin and drypoint. 211 x 160 mm.
Signed and dated: *Rembrandt f. 1654*

FIRST STATE. Etching only.

87 *Museum of Fine Arts, Boston. Gift of Lydia Evans Tunnard in memory of W.G. Russell Allen.*

On double thickness of Japanese tissue.

The breadth and openness of the etched lines in combination with the sheen and translucency of the paper contribute to an effect of all-pervading light.

Colls.: P. Davidsohn (L. 654); F. Seymour Haden (L. 1227); W.G. Russell Allen.

SECOND STATE.
Drypoint strokes have been added to model and describe more literally the head of Christ and the surrounding rays, the apostle at the left, the table, the canopy, and the hat of the other apostle at the right.

88 *Pierpont Morgan Library, New York.*

On European paper without watermark.

Light, which in the first state radiates throughout, is now concentrated around the head of Christ. The drypoint burr is unusually rich, suggesting that this was one of the earliest impressions pulled from the plate in its second state.

Colls.: J. Gibbs (cf. L. 1081 and L. 1125); T. Irwin (L. 1540); J. Pierpont Morgan (L. 1509).

89 *The Art Institute of Chicago. The Clarence Buckingham Collection.*

On Japanese paper.

A more typical impression of this state in that the burr of the drypoint lines has worn somewhat, and the general effect is one of greater balance.

Coll.: C. Schlösser (L. 636).

THIRD STATE
Fine burin hatching which simulates drypoint tone has been added on the table, in the shadows behind the man at the right, and around the feet of the man at the left.

90 *Fogg Art Museum, Harvard University, Cambridge.*

On European paper without watermark.

The drypoint burr has disappeared.

91 Copper plate for CHRIST AT EMMAUS

Mr. and Mrs. Robert Lee Humber, Greenville, N.C., courtesy of the North Carolina Museum of Art, Raleigh.

87.   *Christ at Emmaus. H. 282, first state. Museum of Fine Arts, Boston.*   137

88. *Christ at Emmaus. H. 282, second state. Pierpont Morgan Library.*

89.   *Christ at Emmaus. H. 282, second state. The Art Institute of Chicago.*

90.   *Christ at Emmaus. H. 282, third state. Fogg Art Museum.*

91. *Christ at Emmaus, original copper plate. Mr. and Mrs. Robert Lee Humber.*

Abraham's Sacrifice

H. 283, B. 35, Mz. 184, BB. 55-B
Etching and drypoint. 156 x 131 mm.
Signed and dated: *Rembrandt f. 1655*

ONLY STATE

92 *Museum of Fine Arts, Boston. Harvey D. Parker
    Collection.*

On European paper without watermark.

The character of the etched lines varies widely within
this plate, from the faint mesh of cross-hatching above
Abraham's sword to the boldly drawn and deeply
bitten outlines of the firewood and left foreground.
Drypoint has been employed to complete contours,
the burr adding texture to Abraham's beard and
coloristic effects to his scabbard and to Isaac's clothing
at the far left. Stages in the development of the design
may be seen in faint traces of the previous outlines
of the angel's outspread wing and of the ground below
Isaac which have been incompletely erased by
scraping and burnishing of the plate.

Coll.: H.F. Sewall (L. 1309).

93 *The Art Institute of Chicago. The Clarence
    Buckingham Collection.*

On Japanese paper.

Although this impression was probably printed at the
same time as the above, the ink held by the drypoint
burr spreads more noticeably when printed on the
receptive Japanese paper. There is surface tone here,
particularly on the left background, and on Abraham's
right shoulder and the angel's hand and sleeve.

Colls.: J. Chalon (L. 439); St. John Dent (L. 2373);
E. Schröter (L. 2270); R. Gutekunst (L. 2213a).

92. *Abraham's Sacrifice. H. 283, only state. Museum of Fine Arts, Boston.*

93. *Abraham's Sacrifice. H. 283, only state. The Art Institute of Chicago.*

XXI

Jacob Thomasz. Haaringh

H. 288, B. 275, Mz. 75, BB. 55-E
Drypoint and burin. 200 x 148 mm.
Signed and dated: *Rembrandt 1655*

Haaringh was a lawyer practicing in Utrecht. His father, also portrayed by Rembrandt (Hind 287), was the Amsterdam official who supervised the sale of Rembrandt's possessions at the time of the artist's insolvency in 1657 and 1658.

FIRST STATE

94 *The Metropolitan Museum of Art, New York. Bequest of Mrs. H.O. Havemeyer.*

    Watermark: pascal lamb (see Heawood 2842).

    Heavy surface tone over a complex web of drypoint and burin work creates deep velvety shadows. The tone on Haaringh's forehead has been carefully wiped so as to heighten the modelling. Wiping of the collar provides a light accent that helps to detach the sitter's face from the enveloping darkness.

    Colls.: F. Rechberger, 1806 (L. 2133); Walter Francis, fifth Duke of Buccleuch (L. 402); H.O. Havemeyer.

SECOND STATE

A curtain rod has been added across the window. By means of burnishing, white cuffs have been added to Haaringh's sleeves. The signature and date have been reworked.

95 *Pierpont Morgan Library, New York.*
    A clean wiped impression on Japanese paper which clearly shows the dense network of hatching partly obscured by surface tone in the other two impressions exhibited.

96 *National Gallery of Art, Washington, D.C. Rosenwald Collection.*

    A beautiful, dark impression on Japanese paper with considerable tone. A film of tone is visible on the light areas such as Haaringh's face and the window.

    Colls.: H. Brodhurst (L. 1296); A.F. von Lanna (L. 2773); H.G. Whittemore (L. 1384a); L.J. Rosenwald (L. 1760b).

94.   *Jacob Thomasz. Haaringh. H. 288, first state. The Metropolitan Museum of Art.*

95.   *Jacob Thomasz. Haaringh. H. 288, second state. Pierpont Morgan Library.*

96. *Jacob Thomasz. Haaringh. H. 288, second state. National Gallery of Art.*

XXII

Jan Lutma, The Elder,
Goldsmith and Sculptor

H. 290, B. 276, Mz. 77, BB. 56-C
Etching and drypoint. 196 x 150 mm.
Signed and dated from II onwards: *Rembrandt f. 1656*

Jan Lutma (1584-1669) was a prominent Amsterdam
goldsmith.

FIRST STATE

97 *Museum of Fine Arts, Boston. Harvey D. Parker
    Collection.*

    Watermark: lower half of foolscap with five points
    (see Churchill 355).

    A fine impression on white paper.

    Coll.: W. Esdaile (L. 2617).

98 *Pierpont Morgan Library, New York.*

    This impression is printed on a thin white vellum
    which has shrunk somewhat but has probably changed
    little in color. A stipple effect in the blank areas of
    the background is caused by the hair follicles of the
    vellum. No other impression on vellum has been
    recorded.

    Colls.: G.W. Vanderbilt; J. Pierpont Morgan (L. 1509).

99 *The Metropolitan Museum of Art, New York.*

    The luminous warmth of the Japanese paper on which
    this impression is printed gives a suggestion of light
    that is realized in the second state by the addition of
    a window.

    Colls.: Sir E. Astley (L. 2775); J.J. de Claussin;
    F. Debois, 1841 (L. 985); A. Firmin-Didot; G.C. Graves
    (Sylmaris collection).

SECOND STATE

A deep window embrasure has been added in the background. The engraved inscription "Joannes Lutma Aurifecx
Natus Groningae" appears to the right of Lutma's elbow.
The signature and date appear in the upper left corner
of the window.

100 *The Art Institute of Chicago. The Clarence
    Buckingham Collection.*

    On European paper without watermark.

    Colls.: Berlin Kupferstichkabinett, duplicate (L. 1606);
    W.H.F.K. Graf von Lepell (L. 1672); S. S. Scheikevitch
    (L. 2367).

97.   *Jan Lutma, The Elder, Goldsmith and Sculptor. H. 290, first state. Museum of Fine Arts, Boston.*

98.   Jan Lutma, The Elder, Goldsmith and Sculptor. H. 290, first state. Pierpont Morgan Library, New York.   151

99.   *Jan Lutma, The Elder, Goldsmith and Sculptor. H. 290, first state. The Metropolitan Museum of Art.*

100. *Jan Lutma, The Elder, Goldsmith and Sculptor. H. 290, second state. The Art Institute of Chicago.* 153

XXIII

Saint Francis beneath a Tree, Praying

H. 292, B. 107, Mz. 250, BB. 57-A
Drypoint, etching and burin. 180 x 244 mm.
Signed and dated: *Rembrandt f. 1657*

FIRST STATE. Drypoint only.

101 *Pierpont Morgan Library, New York.*

Printed on a sheet of vellum which has been patched at the upper left, this is one of five known impressions of the first state. The great freedom with which Rembrandt has scratched the image into the plate is paralleled by the bold painterly handling of surface tone. Heavy tone casts a veil of darkness over two-thirds of the sheet. The light triangular area between the saint and the tree trunk is here reduced, anticipating the addition of further landscape detail in the following state. Subtle wiping creates lights which half reveal the crucifix and create an aura around the head of the saint. The area of foliage in the lower left corner has failed to print in full detail.

Colls.: P. Remy, 1749 (L. 2106); Baron J.G. Verstolk van Soelen (L. 2490); J.H. Hawkins; Walter Francis, fifth Duke of Buccleuch (L. 402); G.W. Vanderbilt; J. Pierpont Morgan (L. 1509).

SECOND STATE
The whole plate has been elaborated by etching supplemented with burin work. Particular attention has been given to further description of the landscape setting. A second signature and date have been added over the first.

102 *Museum of Fine Arts, Boston. 1951 Purchase Fund.*

On Japanese paper.

Most early impressions of the second state are characterized by the generous use of surface tone to establish varying relationships between the saint, the crucifix and the landscape. In this impression, saint and crucifix are brought into closer communion by the film of tone which envelops them in shadow.

Coll.: Dukes d'Arenberg (L. 567).

103 *Pierpont Morgan Library, New York.*

An impression on Japanese paper in which a fairly even film of ink covers the entire sheet. A more localized application of tone darkens the saint's robe. On the verso of this impression there is an offset of an old inscription in Dutch, written in a cursive hand. It has yet to be fully deciphered.

Colls.: John Barnard (L. 1419); G. Hibbert (L. 2849); S. Woodburn; J.H. Hawkins; T. Irwin (L. 1540); J. Pierpont Morgan (L. 1509).

104 *National Gallery of Art, Washington, D.C. Rosenwald Collection.*

On Japanese paper.

The whole composition is darkened by a heavy veil of surface tone.

Coll.: L. J. Rosenwald (L. 1760b).

105 *Allen Memorial Art Museum, Oberlin College, Oberlin, Ohio.*

On paper with yellow fibers; perhaps of Indian origin.

A very rich impression but with relatively little surface tone.

Colls.: Heneage Finch, fifth Earl of Aylesford (L. 58); J.H. Hawkins (L. 1471); Walter Francis, fifth Duke of Buccleuch (L. 402); A. Hubert (L. 130); Brayton Ives.

101. *Saint Francis beneath a Tree, Praying. H. 292, first state. Pierpont Morgan Library. Illustration reduced.*

155

101a.   Detail of Saint Francis beneath a Tree, Praying. H. 292, first state. Pierpont Morgan Library.

102a.   Detail of Saint Francis beneath a Tree, Praying. H. 292, second state. Museum of Fine Arts, Boston.

102b.   Detail of Saint Francis beneath a Tree, Praying. H. 292, second state. Museum of Fine Arts, Boston.   157

158   102.   *Saint Francis beneath a Tree, Praying. H. 292, second state. Museum of Fine Arts, Boston. Illustration reduced.*

103. *Saint Francis beneath a Tree, Praying. H. 292, second state. Pierpont Morgan Library. Illustration reduced.*

104.   *Saint Francis beneath a Tree, Praying. H. 292, second state. National Gallery of Art. Illustration reduced.*

105. *Saint Francis beneath a Tree, Praying. H. 292, second state. Allen Memorial Art Museum. Illustration reduced.*   161

XXIV

The Agony in the Garden

H. 293, B. 75, Mz. 225, BB. 57-3
Etching and drypoint. 111 x 84 mm.
Signed and dated: *Rembrandt f. 165-* (about 1657)

ONLY STATE

106 *National Gallery of Art, Washington, D.C.*
Rosenwald Collection.

On European paper; no visible watermark.

An early impression which has been clean wiped.
The rich drypoint burr alone provides tonal effects.

Coll.: L.J. Rosenwald (L. 1760b).

107 *The Metropolitan Museum of Art, New York. Gift of*
Felix M. Warburg and his Family.

On European paper without watermark.

Light surface tone shadows the angel and the sleeping
apostles. By contrast, Christ's face and garment remain
white.

Colls.: J. Webster (L. 1554); F.M. Warburg.

106. *The Agony in the Garden. H. 293, only state. National Gallery of Art.*

107. *The Agony in the Garden. H. 293, only state. The Metropolitan Museum of Art.*   163

XXV

Woman Bathing her Feet at a Brook

H. 298, B. 200, Mz. 140, BB. 58-D
Etching, drypoint and burin. 162 x 80 mm.
Signed and dated: *Rembrandt f. 1658*

ONLY STATE

108 *Museum of Fine Arts, Boston. Harvey D. Parker Collection.*

A clean wiped impression on Japanese paper. The color and texture of the paper suggest warm flesh tones. This effect is seen also in an impression of *Jupiter and Antiope* on Japanese paper (Cat. No. 114).

Coll.: H.F. Sewall (L. 1309).

109 *The Metropolitan Museum of Art, New York. Gift of David Keppel.*

Another impression on Japanese paper distinguished by the use of subtly graded surface tone. The plate has been wiped so as to focus attention on the right side of the torso and thighs. The woman's head and the background are veiled in tone. Yet deeper shadow has been created by an especially heavy layer of tone across her lower legs and the bank.

Colls.: Dr. D.D. Roth (L. 2172); Dr. A. Sträter (L. 787); ⓐ (Unidentified collector's mark).

108.   *Woman Bathing her Feet at a Brook. H. 298, only state. Museum of Fine Arts, Boston.*

109.   *Woman Bathing her Feet at a Brook. H. 298, only state. The Metropolitan Museum of Art.*

XXVI

"Negress" Lying Down

H. 299, B. 205, Mz. 142, BB. 58-E
Etching, drypoint and burin. 81 x 158 mm.
Signed and dated: *Rembrandt f. 1658*

SECOND STATE
Further shading has been added to the pillow and possibly
to the figure.

110 *The Metropolitan Museum of Art, New York. Bequest
of Mrs. H.O. Havemeyer.*

On Japanese paper as are most impressions of this
state.

Fine impressions of this plate are dependent on careful
inking and delicate wiping to model the figure.

Colls.: F. Seymour Haden (L. 1227); H.O. Havemeyer.

111 *National Gallery of Art, Washington, D.C.
Rosenwald Collection.*

On Japanese paper.

Coll.: L.J. Rosenwald (L. 1760b).

THIRD STATE
The blank areas at the upper edge of the plate have been
filled in with hatching.

112 *Pierpont Morgan Library, New York.*
Watermark: *RTO*

Colls.: T.W. Holburne (L. 1265); T. Irwin (L. 1540);
J. Pierpont Morgan (L. 1509).

110. "Negress" Lying Down. H. 299, second state. The Metropolitan Museum of Art.

111. "Negress" Lying Down. H. 299, second state. National Gallery of Art.

112. *"Negress" Lying Down. H. 299, third state. Pierpont Morgan Library.*

XXVII

Jupiter and Antiope: The Larger Plate

H. 302, B. 203, Mz. 143, BB. 59-B
Etching, drypoint and burin. 140 x 205 mm.
Signed and dated: *Rembrandt f. 1659*

FIRST STATE

113 *Pierpont Morgan Library, New York.*

Watermark: *RP*

An impression on white paper in which a film of ink has been left over the entire plate. The impression is unusually rich in drypoint.

Colls.: Sir E. Astley (L. 2775); T. Irwin (L. 1540); J. Pierpont Morgan (L. 1509).

114 *Pierpont Morgan Library, New York.*

On Japanese paper.

An even gray film of ink combines with the luminous yellow paper to produce a color effect peculiar to Rembrandt.

Colls.: G.W. Vanderbilt; J. Pierpont Morgan (L. 1509).

113. *Jupiter and Antiope. H. 302, first state. Pierpont Morgan Library.*

114. *Jupiter and Antiope. H. 302, first state. Pierpont Morgan Library.*

XXVIII

The Woman with the "Arrow"

H. 303, B. 202, Mz. 144, BB. 61-A
Etching, drypoint and burin. 204 x 124 mm.
Signed and dated: *Rembrandt f. 1661*

SECOND STATE

Some additional shading on the woman's cheek, around her feet and on the curtain at the upper right.

115 *The Art Institute of Chicago. The Clarence Buckingham Collection.*

On European paper without watermark.

The various ways in which surface tone is applied in impressions of this state reveal a preoccupation with the relationship of the figure to the background. Here, tone is visible on the curtains of the background and on the left side of the woman's body, while her right side has been wiped clean.

Colls.: C. Schlösser (L. 636); Cabinet Brentano-Birckenstock (L. 345).

116 *National Gallery of Art, Washington, D.C. Rosenwald Collection.*

On European paper; no visible watermark.

An impression in which the distribution of surface tone differs considerably from the previous impression; for example, here tone appears on the knee and the area around it.

Colls.: P. Remy (L. 2173); Sir E. Astley (L. 2775); W. Esdaile (L. 2617); J.-L.-H. Le Secq, called Des Tournelles (L. 1336); H.G. Whittemore (L. 1384a).

117 *Pierpont Morgan Library, New York.*

Watermark: lower point of shield with *WR* below.

A clean wiped impression in which the work on the plate may be clearly seen.

Colls.: Heneage Finch, fifth Earl of Aylesford (L. 58); G.W. Vanderbilt; J. Pierpont Morgan (L. 1509).

THIRD STATE

The signature has been retraced in drypoint and a small blank triangle after the date filled in with hatching.

118 *Pierpont Morgan Library, New York.*

On European paper without watermark.

Light surface tone is visible on the background and on areas of the foreground such as the hanging sleeve.

Colls.: K.F.F. von Nagler (L. 2529); Berlin Kupferstich-kabinett, duplicate (L. 1606); J.C.D. Hebich (L. 1250); T. Irwin (L. 1540); J. Pierpont Morgan (L.1509)

115.   *The Woman with the "Arrow". H. 303, second state. The Art Institute of Chicago.*

116.   *The Woman with the "Arrow". H. 303, second state. National Gallery of Art.*

117.   *The Woman with the "Arrow". H. 303, second state. Pierpont Morgan Library.*

118. *The Woman with the "Arrow". H. 303, third state. Pierpont Morgan Library.*

A Note on Rembrandt Collectors

Most of the Rembrandt etchings now owned by American museums were acquired in sizable blocks from private collectors, either by bequest or gift or by purchase. The Rembrandt holdings of the Morgan Library, the largest and most representative single collection in the country, stem from two major sources. The collection of Theodore Irwin of Oswego, New York, numbering two hundred and seventy-two pieces, was purchased by Mr. Morgan in 1900. A few years later in 1905 negotiations were begun for the sale of one hundred and twelve etchings from the collection of George W. Vanderbilt. Under Pierpont Morgan's son, J.P. Morgan, the Library continued to augment its holdings, the most important additions coming from the collection of Otto Gerstenberg which was dispersed in 1922 in Zurich.

The foundation of the Museum of Fine Arts' print collections was laid in 1897 when 23,000 prints, including many fine Rembrandts, were purchased with funds provided by Harvey D. Parker, from the collection of Henry F. Sewall, a New York businessman who was among the first great American collectors of prints. Other Rembrandts in the present exhibition were given by various members of the families of Francis Bullard, Horatio G. Curtis and W.G. Russell Allen.

The Metropolitan Museum of Art owes the finest of its group of Rembrandt etchings largely to the generosity of two private collectors. The bequest of Mrs. Henry O. Havemeyer in 1929 included thirty-three pieces; twenty years later in 1949, Felix M. Warburg and his family bestowed the choicest of his Rembrandt etchings on the Metropolitan's Print Room.

The benefactions of two collectors likewise account for the greater part of the Rembrandt etchings now in the Print Room of the National Gallery of Art. The gift of Lessing J. Rosenwald in 1943 included a notable series of Rembrandts, handsomely supplemented in 1949 by the group given by R. Horace Gallatin.

The Clarence Buckingham Collection in the Print Room of The Art Institute of Chicago includes not only the Rembrandts acquired by the philanthropist during his lifetime, but also purchases made subsequent to his death in 1913.

These Americans were the spiritual descendants of a long line of European collectors. Some of the names of the latter, which are listed in the catalogue entries, are of particular interest because they form more or less continuous chains of ownership reaching back to Rembrandt's time. Some of the lines of descent seem to reach back to the 1734 sale of Rembrandt etchings owned by Willem Six which are presumed to have come in part from his uncle, Jan Six (1618-1700), who was Rembrandt's friend and patron. At this sale, the Dutch printmaker, Jacob Houbraken (1698-1780) was one of the buyers, and later a part of his Rembrandt prints were acquired by the English painter and etcher, Arthur Pond (ca. 1705-1758), and then by Sir Edward Astley (1729-1802), himself an amateur printmaker. Another collector who is thought to have acquired prints directly from Houbraken is John Barnard (died 1784).

A different chain of ownership is traceable from the widow of the early Rembrandt collector, Valerius Röver (1686-1739). In 1761 his large portfolio of Rembrandt's etched work was sold to the connoisseur and reproductive engraver Cornelis Ploos van Amstel (1726-1798). Some of Ploos van Amstel's Rembrandt prints were reputed to have belonged to Jan Six. Ploos van Amstel's collection was catalogued for public sale by Christian Josi (ca. 1765-1859), but was instead sold privately to the Earl of Aylesford (1786-1855) who not only made imitations of Rembrandt etchings but also formed a great collection of them. Much of Aylesford's collection went to John Haywood Hawkins (1803-1877), a member of Parliament, and from him to the Duke of Buccleuch (1806-1884) whose collection was in turn dispersed by sale. A number of the Buccleuch prints were acquired by George W. Vanderbilt who eventually sold his collection to J. Pierpont Morgan.

Types of Papers Used by Rembrandt

When preparation for this exhibition began in 1967, it was decided that it would be useful to collect information on the watermarks in papers used by Rembrandt for his etchings. Such information was not available at that time in publications on Rembrandt's prints. It was felt that familiarity with the watermarks found in fine early impressions, presumably printed by Rembrandt himself, would be a valuable asset.

Therefore as much information as possible was gathered on the watermarks of Rembrandt etchings in American collections. Many of these impressions were studied in the originals. Particular attention was paid to impressions of the period of about 1640-1660, especially those subjects represented in the exhibition.

All impressions in the Museum of Fine Arts, Boston, the Boston Public Library, the Fogg Art Museum, and most of those in the collections of the Pierpont Morgan Library and the Metropolitan Museum of Art were studied for watermarks. All the etchings in the two-part Nowell-Usticke sale held in 1967 and 1968 at the Parke-Bernet Galleries in New York were similarly inspected. In addition, the lenders to the exhibition, as well as other institutions, generously provided information on the watermarks of their Rembrandt etchings.

The watermarks were either traced or compared to illustrations in published sources. (It is interesting to note that a number of these watermarks corresponded to those on accepted Rembrandt drawings.) The watermarks, the etched subjects and their states were then collated. A tabulation of these is found on pages 181 to 183.

It was hoped that some meaningful correlations might emerge, such as a relationship between the date or type of print and the watermark. This, however, did not happen. Rembrandt's choice of European watermarked papers seems to have been based partly on the type of papers which were available to him in Amsterdam. The visual appearance of the papers and their suitability for printing, as discussed below, were factors in this choice, as was Rembrandt's inclination to experiment with different papers.

More comprehensive information on the watermarks found in Rembrandt's prints is available in Osbert Barnard's studies published in the revised edition of G. Biörklund and O. Barnard, *Rembrandt Etchings: True and False* (1968). His detailed information on Japanese papers is also extremely useful.

Concurrently, with the study of watermarks, we noted the different kinds of paper which were used for fine early impressions: Japanese, "oatmeal", so-called Indian, as well as vellum. Comments on Rembrandt's choice of types of paper, both European and Oriental, for certain prints or certain states, will be found in the catalogue entries. For a more comprehensive discussion, see Christopher White, *Rembrandt as an Etcher* (1969) and the same author's catalogue for the exhibition *The Late Etchings of Rembrandt* (London, 1969).

Especially helpful throughout these studies were Miss Stephanie Loeb of the Museum of Fine Arts, Boston and Francis W. Dolloff and Roy Perkinson, Conservators, who provided much information and assistance. Alexander J. Yow, Conservator at the Pierpont Morgan Library, made tracings of the watermarks of the Library's impressions in the exhibition. Marc Rosen of the Parke-Bernet Galleries was interested and courteous in permitting close study of the Nowell-Usticke impressions. Yasuhiro Iguchi and Money Hickman of the Asiatic Department of the Museum of Fine Arts, Boston, were kind enough to examine the impressions on Oriental papers and analyze the paper type.

EUROPEAN PAPERS

A wide variety of papers of European manufacture were available to Rembrandt for printing his etchings. These papers were of the same fine quality used for books, state documents and correspondence.

As Dutch paper mills did not produce high quality paper until the last quarter of the seventeenth century, most of the paper Rembrandt used came from Germany, Switzerland and France. Amsterdam, an active center for printers and publishers during Rembrandt's lifetime, imported large amounts of foreign made paper, and it was probably possible for Rembrandt to buy his paper in small batches from local importers and dealers as he needed it.

Paper used for etchings must have certain qualities. It must be strong in order to withstand dampening and printing under great pressure. Its surface must be receptive to ink, neither too rough nor too hard. The European papers that Rembrandt used were made of pure rag fibers and tended to change color very little with age, mellowing only from white to warm creamy tones. Moreover, they have been remarkably durable. Some impressions have been washed, bleached or otherwise treated in the intervening three hundred years since their execution, yet are still in good condition.

Seventeenth century papers were handmade. Pulp made of flax or hemp fibers was formed into sheets on wire screens. The characteristic "laid lines" of such paper are the indentations made by the close, parallel wires ("wire lines") and their binding wires ("chain lines") which comprise the screen. A papermaker could produce a distinguishing mark on each sheet by bending wire into any desired image and tying this to the screen. The layer of fibers which forms over this wire shape is thinner and thus the sheets of paper show a translucent image known as a watermark. The wires which form the watermark easily bend out of shape, or break and have to be replaced, so that exact correspondence of form is seldom seen. There are, for example, bound books with many leaves displaying watermarks that are similar but not precisely identical. Sometimes both a watermark and a smaller and simpler mark, the countermark, were placed on opposite halves of the sheet.

The watermark alone does not provide a reliable basis for reaching conclusions as to the characteristics of a paper. Individual sheets, even of the same type and from the same lot, may vary slightly in thickness because they are handmade. In this exhibition, papers range from the smooth, thin papers with Foolscap watermarks used for printing the *Landscape with Farmbuildings and a Tower* (Cat. Nos. 20, 21) to the heavier weight and rougher surface of the large sheets used for *Christ Crucified between the Two Thieves* (Cat. Nos. 54, 56) and *Christ Presented to the People* (Cat. No. 68), watermarked respectively with the Strasburg bend and Strasburg lily.

Watermarks and countermarks may be symbols or devices for the manufacturer, the place of manufacture, the lot, the seller or the customer. Their precise interpretation is often difficult. They tend to be conventional in form and were used by different papermakers for decades with little change. In addition, famous papermakers' marks may be retained by their mills long after their lifetime or may sometimes be pirated by mills of another country. While it has been suggested by some authorities that most of the papers Rembrandt used were of French origin, H. Voorn, in a study limited to paper mills of North Holland, maintains that before 1650 most papers used there were imported from Germany and Switzerland, and that it was only after the mid-century that French papers became those most commonly available (*De papiermolens in de provincie Noord-Holland*, 1960). As mentioned above, the watermark is not always a totally reliable indication of where a paper was made. Nevertheless, the frequency among Rembrandt's prints of the Strasburg lily and the Foolscap watermarks, both originally German marks, and of certain Swiss marks, seems to bear out Voorn's observations.

Various encyclopedic studies of watermarks and their correlation with dated or datable manuscripts, documents and printed texts have been made. The classic work is *Les Filigranes* by C.M. Briquet (Geneva, 1907.) Especially relevant to the papers of Rembrandt are the studies of seventeenth and eighteenth century papers and their watermarks by E. Heawood *(Watermarks,* Hilversum, 1950) and by W.A. Churchill *(Watermarks in Paper in the XVII and XVIII Centuries,* Amsterdam, 1935).

The method of dating followed in these studies is, of necessity, based on when the paper was used rather than on an exact knowledge of the years of its manufacture. In some cases these dates are estimated rather than assigned on the basis of any known use. Usually the watermark date is contemporary with or slightly earlier than the date of the print. Several examples of exceptions are discussed below.

The watermark may have been assigned a date later than the print. The watermark on an impression of the first state of *Christ Crucified between the Two Thieves* (Cat. No. 54) is comparable only to one found in a book published in Amsterdam in 1670 (Heawood 146) or to an early eighteenth century mark (Heawood 63). However, since Rembrandt's plate is dated 1653, it is certain that this impression antedates the book. In this case, the explanation may be that the watermark is probably not identical with the two recorded by Heawood. As will be seen in the *Table of Watermarks*, this is the only print in the exhibition for which a closer correlation between the date of the plate and the dating of the watermark was not found.

When the watermarks are more nearly identical, comparison of the dates of the watermarks and of the prints are more revealing. For example, an impression of the first state of *Clement de Jonghe* (1651) in The Art Institute of Chicago is printed on paper with a watermark which is also found in a book printed in 1637 (see Heawood 585); similarly an impression of *The Good Samaritan* (1633) in the Museum of Fine Arts, Boston, is on a paper with a watermark which occurs in a book published in Amsterdam in 1594 (see Heawood 481, Briquet 2291). This seems to suggest that Rembrandt sometimes printed on older papers. It is perhaps significant that in the 1656 inventory of Rembrandt's belongings (made because he was declared bankrupt) are noted, *"nog een antieck boeck ledich"* (another old book, empty) and *"een leech cunstboeck* (an empty sketchbook) and *"een dito als voiren"* (another like the above), (Hofstede de Groot, *Urkünden über Rembrandt*, item 169, nos. 221, 242, 243).

Commonly, impressions of the same state appear on papers with a variety of watermarks. At times, papers with the same watermark were used for printing plates executed ten years or more apart as may be deduced from the table on page 181. In some rare instances, a number of impressions are found on sheets with identical watermarks. Of twelve impressions of *The Three Trees* (H. 205) in the United States, six are on the same paper, watermarked with a Strasburg lily, the letters *PR* below, and the countermark *WK*. It may be possible to discover similar correlations. However, with the data now available, there does not seem to be an expressed pattern of Rembrandt's usage of European watermarked papers.

OATMEAL OR CARTRIDGE PAPER *(kardoes papier; papier cardouce)*

This paper, which is of European manufacture, has a gray or buff color occasioned by the presence of many unbleached fibers. Not intended as a fine writing paper or a printing paper, it was nonetheless prized by artists for its tonal qualities. In this exhibition, there are impressions of *Faust in His Study* (Cat. No. 47) and of *St. Jerome Reading in an Italian Landscape* (Cat. No. 52) printed on oatmeal paper. It sometimes shows a watermark of a six- or eight-petalled flower within a circle.

INDIAN PAPER

Five known impressions of the first state of *Jan Asselyn* (H. 227) are printed on an off-white paper, without prominent laid lines, but with yellow fibers throughout (Bibliothèque Nationale, Paris; Pierpont Morgan Library; Rijksmuseum; Lessing J. Rosenwald Collection, National Gallery of Art; Städelesches Institut, Frankfort). One is exhibited here (Cat. No. 1). At least two impressions of *Saint Francis beneath a Tree, Praying* (H. 292) appear on this paper (Bibliothèque Nationale, Paris, first state; Metropolitan Museum of Art, second state). This paper has been compared to that on which Indian miniatures are executed, and it is possibly of Indian origin. It is not of Japanese manufacture.

JAPANESE PAPER

From about 1647 onwards, Rembrandt frequently printed on papers of non-European origin. Although these papers vary in weight and color, study and analysis have shown most of them to be of Japanese manufacture and composed entirely of the fibers of the inner bark of the *gampi* plant. Japanese paper was not commonly imported into Europe, but its use for local records by Dutch and other European companies in the Far East is known; from 1639 until 1854, the Dutch alone had access to Japanese harbors. Documentary evidence exists for small lots of Japanese paper aboard only two westbound ships of the Dutch East India Company: one shipment in 1643 and another in the following year. Probably one or the other of these lots reached Holland and was the source from which Rembrandt got his Japanese papers.

The range of color in the Japanese *gampi* paper used by Rembrandt is remarkable. It varies from nearly pure white,

through pale yellows to dark golds; there are shades of warm and pearly grays as well. The weight varies from a thin, semi-transparent tissue to a sturdy, dense sheet. Japanese papers are without watermark, although the lighter weight sheets show laid lines from the bamboo screens on which the paper is formed.

Often, two sheets have been mounted together, probably for added strength. It is usually difficult to ascertain if this was done at the place of manufacture, or by Rembrandt himself, either before or during printing. In the present exhibition, one impression printed on the very lightest weight paper *(Christ at Emmaus,* Cat. No. 87) was pulled with two sheets together, for the ink seeped through onto the upper surface of the second sheet. Rembrandt selected the thinnest and whitest paper on which to print this subject, one of the most simply etched and full of a clear and radiant light. The middle weights and neutral tones of Japanese paper are found in the exhibition among impressions of *Christ with the Sick around Him* (Cat. Nos. 10-13), and *Saint Francis beneath a Tree, Praying* (Cat. Nos. 102-104); the clearest and warmest golden tones occur in the papers utilized for the nude subjects (Cat. Nos. 108-111, 114).

Aside from the pleasures of color and texture it affords, the quality that makes *gampi* paper so unusual and eminently appropriate for pulling prints is its soft surface which receives ink readily under minimum pressure, and so does not wear down fine drypoint lines and burr as quickly as rougher paper surfaces tend to do. Japanese paper expands when dampened and shrinks when dried, more so than European papers. Thus, the plate measurements of an impression on Japanese paper will often be two to three millimeters smaller in both dimensions as compared with those of the same subject printed on a European paper.

VELLUM

Sometimes referred to as parchment, which technically speaking is an inner lining only of lambskin, vellum is the stretched, scraped and treated skin of young animals, usually calf, kid or lamb. It is absorbent and takes inks well, but sometimes has a tendency to yellow with age and under certain conditions to shrink. Although finished drawings on vellum were not unusual in seventeenth century Holland, etchings or engravings printed on vellum were a rare occurrence outside of Rembrandt's work. In this exhibition, impressions on vellum include *Christ Crucified between the Two Thieves* (Cat. Nos. 55, 57), *The Entombment* (Cat. No. 81), *Jan Lutma* (Cat. No. 98) and *Saint Francis beneath a Tree, Praying* (Cat. No. 101).

Table of Watermarks

In this table, reference has been confined almost exclusively to fine impressions or to early states of the etchings, which were almost certainly printed by Rembrandt. Not all of these are in the exhibition. The time span has been kept to that which the exhibition encompasses, roughly from the mid 1640's to the early 1660's. Earlier subjects are included when they bear the same watermark; these impressions are usually of the final state and may represent later printings by Rembrandt.

It was decided to refer to general types, mostly reproduced in Heawood and Churchill, rather than reproduce a large number of variant watermarks from the etchings themselves. A few representative types are illustrated, somewhat reduced in size.

Strasburg lily in shield surmounted by crown

1. With *PR* below; countermark *WK*. See Heawood 1663-65 (book published in Amsterdam, 1646).

   Hind 43, 178^{I}, 181^{II} (2 impressions), 205 (6 impressions), 233^{I}, 233^{II}, (2 impressions), 244^{IV} 263^{II}, 264^{II}.

   WK only   H. 186, 231^{I}, 263^{II}.

2. See Heawood 1721A (Schieland, 1614). With countermark *IV*   H. 236^{II} (2 impressions).

3. With *WR* below See Heawood 1768, 1769 (England ?, Schieland, 1616), Heawood 1766 (Schieland, 1625).   H. 103^{II}, 111^{I}, 134^{II}, 143^{IV}, 182^{II}, 226^{II}, 266^{IV}.

4. See Heawood 1730 (book, Amsterdam, 1646).   H. 249.

5. With *BA* below See Heawood 1771, 1772 (book, Amsterdam, 1646).   H. 111^{II}, 127^{I}.

6. With *IHS* See Heawood 1772 (book, Amsterdam, 1646); Heawood 1780 (book, London, 1680).   H. 271^{VII}, 260^{II}.

7. Very large. See Heawood 1784 (book, Amsterdam, 1683); Heawood 1811 (book, Amsterdam, 1727).   H. 163^{III}, 236^{II}, 292^{II}.

8. See Churchill 400 (1624).   H. 233^{II}.

9. Large lily   H. 205, 232^{II}, 236^{II} (2 impressions).

10. Lily (no other information)   H. 203^{I}A, 203^{II}A.

Foolscap

11. Large, with 5 points, *D* below. See Heawood 1929 (Holland, 1629); Churchill 342 (17th century).   H. 256 and counterproof.

12. 5 points, small bells. See Heawood 1923 (1645).   H. 244^{III}.

13. 5 points, large bells; countermark *LB*. See Heawood 1921-22 (Dutch 1648-51); Churchill 344 (1649).   H. 120^{III}, 213.

    Countermark *LB* only   H. 213, 239^{II}, 235^{IV}.

    Variant, without *LB* countermark   H. 244^{II}, 235^{III}, 246^{III}; probably also on H. 52, 101^{IV}, 145, 180^{II}, 203.

14. 5 points, large bells. See Churchill 337 (1651 manuscript).   H. 109^{III}, 281^{II}.

15. 5 points, 4 large bells, braided hair. See Churchill 355 (1656 manuscript).   H. 267^{II} (2 impressions), 282^{II}, 290^{I}.

16. 5 points, 5 bells, braid, with *ID* below. See Heawood 1964 (1660's).   H. 52^{II}.

17. 7 points, 7 small bells, *BD* below. See Heawood 2004 (1659-90); Churchill 346 (17th century).   H. 279, 281^{IV} (2 impressions).

18. Small, head only See Heawood 2035 (book, Amsterdam, 1667).   H. 157^{I}, 259^{I}.

19. Foolscap (no other information)   H. 210^{I}, 212, 232^{II}, 239^{II}, 241^{I}, 241^{II}, 245^{III}, 259^{I}, 275^{I}, 276^{I}, 276^{II}, 301^{I}.

Strasburg bend in shield surmounted by lily

20. See Heawood 141 (Holland, 1616).   H. 101^{I}A, 126^{I}, 128^{V}, 172, 225^{I}, 225^{II}, 288^{I}.

21. See Heawood 146 (book, Amsterdam, 1670); 63 (early 18th century).   H. 270^{I}, 270^{II}, 270^{III}.

22. No further information   H. 277^{IV}.

Amsterdam Arms (crowned shield with three crosses flanked by lions rampant)

23. See Churchill 4 (1659).   H. 290^{I} (2 impressions).

1

2

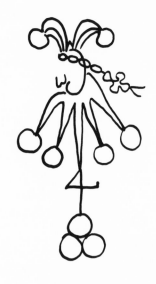

15

20

28

31

Watermarks identified by their numbers from the *Table of Watermarks*. Reduced to 59 per cent of actual size.

24. See Churchill 5, with countermark *IFD* (1662); Heawood 426 (1665).

H. 181, 241^{II}, probably 257^{II} and 302^{I}.

    IFD only

H. 242.

25. See Churchill 1 (1635 manuscript); 10 (1669 manuscript) and 11 (1670); also Heawood 342-345 (1670's-'80's, Dutch manuscripts).

H. 163, 294^{III}, 302^{I}.

    With PB countermark

H. 267^{II}.

26. Amsterdam Arms (no further information)

H. 176^{II}, 183^{II}, 257^{II}, 265^{II}.

Quartered coat-of-arms

27. See Heawood 585 (book, 1637).

H. 251^{I}, 252^{I}.

28. Quartered coat-of-arms. Not found in Heawood.

H. 260^{I}.

Bunch of grapes

29. See Heawood 2227 (book, Paris, 1621).

H. 271^{IV}, 271^{VII}.

Pascal lamb in crowned shield

30. See Heawood 2842 (Schieland, 1649).

H. 162^{II}, 188, 249 (2 impressions), 251^{I}, 251^{II}, 257^{I} (2 impressions), 288^{I}.

31. See Heawood 2843 (Schieland, 1648-51).

H. 220^{I}, 251^{III} (2 impressions), 252^{I}.

Cockatrice and RP

32. See Churchill 286 (Basel, 1630).

H. 53^{III}, 90, 165, 176^{II}, 182^{I}, 182^{II}, 185^{I} (2 impressions), 185^{II}, 204^{I}.

Letters

33. *WK* (no further information), perhaps countermark of lily, no. 1, above.

H. 186, 202^{V}, 203^{II}, 210, 232^{II}.

34. *IHS* (no further information)

H. 226^{II}.

35. *LB* (no further information), perhaps countermark of foolscap, no. 13, above.

H. 179, 209^{III}, 239^{II}, 263^{IV}.

36. *P* over *H* (no further information)

H. 237 (3 impressions).

Lion in Oval with BM below

37. See Heawood 3142 (London, about 1689).

H. 234^{II}, 260^{I}, 273^{I}, 280^{I}.

Coat-of-Arms with bend

38. See Churchill 268 (manuscript, 1620).

H. 267^{II}.

Explanation of Technical Terms

In the *etching* process the copper plate is coated with a resinous ground, impervious to acid. The etching needle, with which the artist draws, easily scratches through the ground to delineate the image. When the plate is exposed to or immersed in acid, the acid corrodes or *bites* only into the exposed areas where the etching needle has drawn lines. Accidental or *foul biting* results when acid penetrates a weak area of ground. Before printing, the ground is removed from the plate, leaving a clean copper surface with the etched lines depressed into it.

Drypoint is the process in which a sharp point is used to draw directly into the surface of the plate. The copper which is displaced from the furrow made by the point is thrown up beside the furrow and this rough ridge of copper is known as *burr*. The burr, which prints as a dark velvety accent, wears down quickly under the pressure of printing.

In the *engraving* process a sharp metal tool called a *burin* or *graver* is used to incise lines into the plate. This square or lozenge-shaped bar of steel, set into a handle, makes a V-shaped furrow in the copper plate.

Scraping and *burnishing* are means by which a printmaker can remove lines which have already been made in the plate. The *scraper* is a sharp, knife-like instrument used to erase lines by lowering the surface of the copper. The *burnisher* is a tool used to smooth down roughened areas which have been scraped; it can also be used to lighten certain areas by reducing the depth of the lines.

To *print* copper plates which have been bitten or incised by any of the foregoing methods, thick ink is spread over the plate and forced into the depressed lines. The plate is then *wiped* with a cloth or the hand to remove excess ink. Any film of ink which is left on the surface of the plate is known as *plate tone* or *surface tone*. Ink may also cling to the drypoint *burr* and print as soft blurry lines or areas. The inked plate and a dampened sheet of paper are then run through a roller-bed press under heavy pressure, and the image transferred in reverse to the paper. A *counterproof* may be taken at this point by running the freshly printed impression through the press with a second sheet of paper. The image thus transferred is in the same direction as the image on the plate. This counterproof sheet can be useful as an aid in making corrections or additions to the plate.

An *impression* is a single pull from a plate. A *state* is any stage in the development of a print at which impressions are taken. States change only with the addition or removal of lines on the plate. Differences in the paper used for printing or variations in the amount of ink tone left on the surface of the plate when it is printed do not constitute a change in state.

ERRATA

Page 10, fourth paragraph	*read*	Finally, in the seventh state, he achieved what he seems to have been looking for earlier – a just and very complex balance of importance between the Christ whom Pilate has placed on trial and the ordinary individuals who at that moment are deciding to condemn Him to death.
Page 12, second paragraph	*read*	The so-called Indian paper, which appears infrequently in Rembrandt's work, is to be seen in two prints in this exhibition, a first state of *Jan Asselyn* (Cat. No. 1) and a second state of *Saint Francis beneath a Tree, Praying* (Cat. No. 105).
Page 13	*read*	White Christopher White, *Rembrandt as an Etcher*, London, 1969, 2 vols.
Page 42, Cat. No. 21	*read*	A light even film of ink over the entire plate creates a tonal effect similar to that achieved by printing on Japanese paper, as in Cat. No. 19.
Page 136, Cat. No. 91	*add*	*Coll.:* Basan.
Page 180, under Indian Paper	*read*	At least three impressions of *Saint Francis beneath a Tree, Praying* appear on this paper (Bibliothèque Nationale, Paris, first state; Metropolitan Museum of Art, New York, second state, and Allen Memorial Art Museum, Oberlin, Ohio, here exhibited as Cat. No. 105).
Page 181	*add*	to number 7 of Watermark table: Hind 260^{II}.
Page 183	*add*	to number 33 of Watermark table: Hind 281^{III}.